Bright Sparks

CJFallon

Published by
CJ FALLON
Ground Floor – Block B
Liffey Valley Office Campus
Dublin 22
Ireland

ISBN: 978-0-7144-1368-6

Design and Editorial Content
©
CJ Fallon

First Printing April 2001
This Reprint September 2016

Stories

The walk

'You need a walk, William,' said my sister Jane.

'No, I don't,' I said.

'Yes, you do,' said Jane.

'I'll come too.

We can take Pepper with us.'

'I don't feel like it,' I said.

'I do,' said Jane, 'and I can make you take us for a walk'.

'No you can't,' I said.

'I'm taller and I'm bigger.'

'But you're not stronger,' said Jane.

'Oh yes I am,' I said.

'I'm taller and bigger and stronger.'

'You're taller.

You're bigger.

But I am stronger,' said Jane.

'I am so strong I can make everyone in this house come here in an instant,' she added.

'So can I,' I said. 'Watch me.'

I went and found Mum.

'Come with me,' I said.

'I'm busy,' said Mum.

I pulled on her chair.

I pulled and I pulled.

7

I pulled so hard that I dragged the chair all the way to the living-room.

But Mum went back to work.

I found Dad.

'Come with me,' I said.

'I'm busy,' said Dad.

I tugged on his coat.

I tugged and I tugged.

I tugged so hard that I pulled that coat all the way to the living-room.

But Dad went back to work.
I found Grandma.
'Come with me,' I said.
'I'm watching TV,' said Grandma.
I pushed on the bed.
I pushed and I pushed.
I pushed so hard that the bed almost went through the door.
But it stuck.

I found Pepper.
'Come with me,' I said to the dog.
I pulled on the rug.
I pulled and I pulled.
I pulled so hard that I pulled Pepper all the way to the living-room.
But Pepper ran away.

'Well!' said Jane.

'You have a chair, a coat and a rug,
but no people and no dog.

Now it's my turn. Watch this!'

Jane stood still for a minute.

She took a deep breath.

Then she started to cry, very loudly.

Before I could blink an eye — into the room
ran Mum, Dad, Grandma and Pepper the dog.

'I'm OK,' said Jane.

'I'm just fine.

And *I'm* the strongest!'

Mum's face went pink.
Dad's face turned red.
Grandma turned purple.
'Out!' said Mum and Dad and Grandma.
'You both need some fresh air before lunch.'
'Yes, William,' said Jane.
'We need a walk.
And we can take Pepper with us.'
'Drats!' I said.

From *I am Reading: Watch Out William*
by Kady Macdonald Denton, Kingfisher

Blarney Blasts

1 What do you think about what Jane did in the story? Tell a partner.

2 Tell about the time when you were made do something that you didn't want to do.

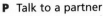

P Talk to a partner
C Talk to your class
G Talk in a group
T Debate in teams

Log Jogging

My favourite moment in the story was...

Tale and Detail

1 Who is telling this story?
2 Name the people who lived in the house.
3 What was Grandma doing?
4 Where was Pepper?
5 What colour did Dad's face turn?

Undercover Work

1 Was Jane really stronger than William? Why do you think so?
2 Why did William not yell?
3 Why did the grown-ups send the children out?
4 How did Jane make everyone come to her?
5 Write all that William did to show he was strong.

Word Wizardry

These are all naming words:

| chair | coat | rug | dog | eye |

Write sentences containing each of these words.

Guess what these naming words are.

You can wear it on your head. _____

It lives in a nest. _____

You use it to write with. _____

You sleep in it. _____

Did anyone in your class guess a different naming word?

Surf the Imagination

Write about something you had to do and you did not want to do it.

Mouse Search

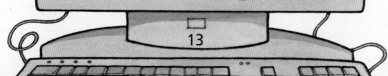

1 Find out what pets your classmates have at home.
2 Make a barchart of the results for your classroom.

You could use your computer for this.

13

Mr Cool

Ricky wanted to be a rock star. He was brilliant at singing. He was brilliant at dancing. He looked brilliant too. Ricky had floppy fair hair that fell into his blue eyes. Ricky always wore blue denim. Ricky looked cool.

Micky wanted to be a rock star. He was terrific at singing. He was terrific at dancing. He looked terrific too. Micky had long red hair and wicked green eyes. Micky always wore black. Micky looked cool.

Nicky wanted to be a rock star. He was fantastic at singing. He was fantastic at dancing. He looked fantastic too. Nicky had curly black hair and big brown eyes. Nicky always wore leather. Nicky looked cool.

Kevin wanted to be a rock star. He wasn't great at singing. He wasn't great at dancing. He didn't look great either. Kevin had straight mousey hair and grey eyes. Kevin always wore a jumper, knitted by his Nan, and tracksuit bottoms. Kevin didn't look cool. But he had a great smile.

Ricky and Micky and Nicky formed a band.
'Can I be in the band too?' asked Kevin. Ricky and
Micky and Nicky weren't sure. 'You're a nice guy,
Kevin. But you're not that great at singing,'
said Ricky. Kevin smiled bravely. Ricky felt bad.
'We do like you, Kevin. But you're not that great at
dancing,' said Micky. Kevin smiled bravely.
Micky felt bad. 'You can't help it, Kevin. You just
don't look cool,' said Nicky. Kevin smiled bravely.

15

Nicky felt bad. 'I wish I could be in your band,' said Kevin, still smiling. 'Go on, you guys. Let me be in the band. I'll try hard at singing. I'll try hard at dancing. I'll try hard to look cool.' Ricky and Micky and Nicky still weren't sure. 'My nan's got a basement,' said Kevin. 'We could practise there. My nan won't mind a bit.' Ricky and Micky and Nicky didn't have a good place to practise.

Ricky lived in a bungalow. Ricky's mum and dad moaned and groaned when the boys in the band started playing.

Micky lived in a house with a lot of pets. All the pets howled and yowled when the boys in the band started playing.

Nicky lived in a flat. Nicky's neighbours came to his door and huffed and puffed when the boys in the band started playing. 'Could we practise in your nan's basement any time?' Ricky asked Kevin. 'You bet,' said Kevin. 'Right,' said Ricky. 'You can be in the band then, Kevin. OK, Micky?' 'OK with me,' said Micky. 'OK, Nicky?' 'OK with me,' said Nicky. 'Count yourself one of the band, Kevin,' said Ricky. 'G-r-e-a-t!' said Kevin, and he smiled and smiled and smiled.

From *I Am Reading: Mr Cool*
by Jacqueline Wilson, Kingfisher

Blarney Blasts

1 Imagine you are Kevin's nan. Tell your neighbour about the new band that practises in your basement. What do you say?

2 Act out the scene with Ricky, Micky and Nicky after Kevin asked them if he could join their band.

Log Jogging

I liked / disliked this story because…

Tale and Detail

1 Name the boys in the story.
2 Which of the boys in the story
   (a) always wore leather?
   (b) always wore blue denim?
   (c) always wore black?
   (d) always wore a jumper?
3 What did the pets do when the boys in the band started playing?
4 Who had floppy hair?
5 Where did Nicky live?

Undercover Work

1 Why did Ricky, Micky and Nicky feel badly?
2 Why did Kevin smile?
3 Why did the boys let Kevin join the band?
4 Do you think they were right?
5 Who did Kevin live with?
   Why do you say this?

Word Wizardry

In this story Ricky, Micky and Nicky are singing, dancing and playing. Kevin is always smiling.

These are all **doing** words:

singing	dancing	playing	smiling
eating	dreaming	knitting	chasing

Write sentences containing each of the **doing** words. Write five **doing** words for when you play in the yard or for when you are at home in the evening.

Surf the Imagination

Imagine that you are Kevin.
Draw a picture of the band.
Write about the clothes you like to wear or write about one of your friends' clothes.

Mouse Search

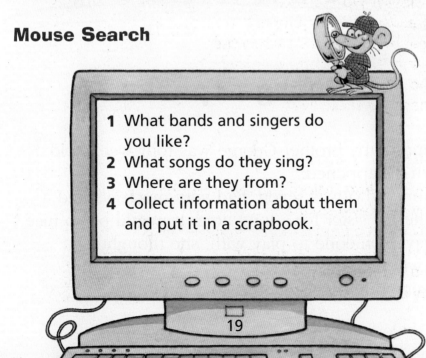

1 What bands and singers do you like?
2 What songs do they sing?
3 Where are they from?
4 Collect information about them and put it in a scrapbook.

19

George speaks

Laura's baby brother George was four weeks old when it happened.

Laura, who was seven, had very much wanted a brother or sister for a long time. It would be so nice to have someone to play with, she thought.

But when George was born, she wasn't so sure.

Everybody — her mother and father, the

grandparents, uncles, aunts, friends — made such a fuss of him. And all of them said how beautiful he was. Laura didn't think he was. How could anyone with a round red face and a squashy nose and little tiny eyes all sunken in fat be called beautiful? She looked at him as he lay asleep in his carry-cot.

'Don't wake George up, will you?' her mother had said. 'I'll be in the kitchen if you want me.'

'I won't wake you,' Laura said to the sleeping baby. 'And I don't want to sound rude. But I must

tell you something. You look just like a little pig.'

And that was when it happened.

The baby opened his eyes and stared straight at her.

'Pig yourself,' he said.

Laura gasped. A shiver ran up her spine and her toes tingled.

'What did you say?' she whispered.

'I said, "Pig yourself",' said George.
'You're not deaf, are you?'

'No,' said Laura. 'No, it's just that I didn't expect
you to say anything.'

'Why not?'

'Well, babies don't say proper words. They only
make noises, like Goo-goo or Blur-blur or Wah.'

'Is that a fact?' said the baby.

'Yes,' said Laura. 'It is. However can you talk like
that when you're only four weeks old? It's amazing!
I must run and tell Mum.'

She turned to dash out of the room.

'Laura!' said the baby sharply.

Laura turned back.

'Yes, George?' she said.

The baby looked at her very severely, his forehead creased into a little frown.

'On no account are you to tell our mother,' he said. 'Or anyone else for that matter. This is a secret between you and me. Do you understand?'

'Yes, George,' said Laura.

'I've been waiting for some time now,' said George, 'to speak to you on your own. This is the first proper chance I've had, what with feeding and bathing and nappy-changing and people coming to see me all the time. And talk about making noises — that's all some of them do. They bend over me with silly grins on their faces, and then they come out with a load of rubbish. "Who's booful den?" "Who's a gorgeous Georgeous Porgeous?" "Diddums wassums Granny's ickle treasure?" It's an insult to the English language.'

'But George,' said Laura, 'how do you know the English language?'

'Well, I'm English, aren't I?'

'Yes, but how did you learn it?'

'Same way as you, I imagine. Listening to grown-ups talking. I wasn't born yesterday, you know.'

'But you're only four weeks old,' said Laura. 'How did you learn so quickly?'

'I'm a quick learner,' said George.

He waved his little arms and kicked his pudgy legs in the air.

'Talking's a piece of cake,' he said. 'Trouble is, I haven't learned to control my body very well yet. In fact, I'm afraid we'll have to postpone the rest of this conversation until another time.'

'Why?' asked Laura.

'I'm wet,' said George.

'Oh,' said Laura. 'Shall I go and tell Mummy you need changing?'

'Use your brains, Laura,' said George. 'You couldn't have known unless I'd told you, could you? You keep quiet. I'll tell her.'

'But you said it was going to be a secret between the two of us — you being able to talk, I mean.'

'So it is,' said George. 'I'll tell her in the way she expects. I've got her quite well trained,' and he shut his eyes and yelled 'Wah! Wah! Wah!' at the top of his voice.

His mother came in.

'What de matter with Mummy's lubbly lickle lambie?' she said.

She picked George up and felt him.

'Oh, he's soaking!' she said. 'No wonder he was crying, poor pettikins!'

She smiled at Laura as she changed the baby's nappy.

'It's the only way they can let you know there's something wrong, isn't it?' she said.

'Yes, Mummy,' said Laura.

She caught George's eye as he lay across his mother's lap. It was no surprise to her that he winked.

George Speaks by Dick King-Smith, Penguin Books

Blarney Blasts

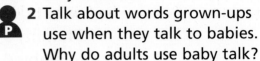

P **1** How do babies tell people what they want?

P **2** Talk about words grown-ups use when they talk to babies. Why do adults use baby talk?

Log Jogging

I wonder why...

Tale and Detail

1 How did Laura describe George?

2 How did George let his mother know that he was wet?

3 What were the first words George spoke in the story?

4 What was George lying in?

5 Where was their mother when George began speaking to Laura?

Undercover Work

1 Everybody made a great fuss of little George. How did Laura feel about that?

2 Why was Laura so surprised when George spoke?

3 What keeps babies busy?

4 Why could George not control his body very well?

5 Which room do you think George was in? Why do you say this?

Lubbly lickle lambie are examples of baby talk.
Can you find more in the story?

Surf the Imagination

1 When you were a baby, if you could have told your parents what name you wanted, what would you have chosen? Why?
2 Draw a cartoon story called George speaks.

Mouse Search

Find out
(a) when you said your first word and what it was
(b) when you first walked
(c) what was your favourite toy when you were a baby
(d) habits you had as a baby
(e) people you liked
(f) what you liked to do
(g) foods you liked
(h) colours you liked.

29

Oisín in Tír na nÓg

One morning the Fianna were going hunting. They were standing on the shores of Loch Léin, waiting for the hunt to begin when they saw the most beautiful woman they had ever seen coming towards them. She had golden hair which almost reached her toes, and her eyes were as blue as the sky. Her dress was brown and there were stars around the neck and hem. She was riding a strong white horse.

'Who are you, and why have you come to Ireland?' Fionn called to her as soon as she was near.

'I am Niamh, the daughter of the King of Tír na nÓg,' she said. 'I have come to Ireland to find your son, Oisín. I have heard of his courage and of his poems and songs,

and I want to marry him and bring him back with me to
Tír na nÓg.' Then she turned to Oisín. 'Tír na nÓg is a
happy country,' she said. 'There is hunting there and
fishing, and everyone is young. If you come with me,
you will have everything you could wish for, and you
will never grow old.'

'I will come with you,' said Oisín, and got up behind
her on the white horse. The Fianna were very sad when
they saw that he was going. Oisín was one of their
greatest heroes and he was their poet and story-teller.

'I will come back soon,' he promised, and then he and
Niamh set off.

They travelled quickly. The horse galloped over land

31

and sea. At last they arrived at a country where the grass
was greener and the sky was bluer than Oisín had
ever seen.

'This is Tír na nÓg,' said Niamh. They were met by the
king and queen who welcomed Oisín. Then they all
feasted for seven days and seven nights, and on the last
night, Niamh and Oisín were married.

Oisín was happy in Tír na nÓg. He hunted and
feasted, as Niamh had promised, and he told stories
about Fionn and the Fianna. Time passed quickly and
Oisín felt he had only been in Tír na nÓg three years,
but, in fact, he had been there far, far longer. One day
he began to feel homesick.

'Niamh,' he said, 'I want to go back to Ireland to visit the Fianna'. Niamh looked sad, but she gave Oisín her white horse.

'Be careful,' she warned him. 'Whatever happens, do not get off the horse; if you do, you will never come back to Tír na nÓg.' Oisín promised to do as she said, and he set off.

Ireland seemed to have changed when Oisín arrived, but he pressed on to look for the Fianna. As he was riding through Gleann na Smól, he saw some men pushing a big stone. The men looked very small to Oisín and they were having a lot of trouble with the stone. Oisín rode over to them.

33

'I will move that stone for you,' he said. He was so very big that he terrified the men. Oisín bent down, leaning over his horse's back. He picked up the stone and flung it away. But he was too heavy for the girth of the saddle. It broke and Oisín fell on to the ground. As soon as he touched the ground, he changed from a young, handsome soldier into a wrinkled old man.

The men he had helped picked him up and carried him to a house nearby. There they told their story to

a holy man. Oisín told them who he was and what had happened him.

'Where are Fionn and the Fianna?' he asked.

'It is three hundred years since Fionn lived in Ireland,' the holy man told him. Oisín lived there until he died, but before he died, he told many stories about Fionn and the Fianna, and that way he made sure that they would not be forgotten in Ireland.

Oisín in Tír na nÓg, Traditional

35

Blarney Blasts

1 What would you like most about *Tír na nÓg*?

2 Imagine your own magical place. What would it be like?

Log Jogging

I felt sorry for…

Tale and Detail

1 Where were Oisín and the Fianna hunting?

2 Describe Niamh.

3 What was special about *Tír na nÓg*?

4 How long did the feast last?

5 What happened when Oisín fell off the horse?

Undercover Work

1 Who was Fionn?

2 When did Oisín say that he would be back?

3 Why did Oisín think he had been in *Tír na nÓg* for only three years?

4 Why did Oisín return to Ireland?

5 What do you think the men were going to do with the big stone that they were rolling?

6 How do we come to know stories from long ago?

36

Word Wizardry

The horse galloped over land and sea.

The **naming** words in this sentence are *horse*, *land* and *sea*, but *galloped* is a **doing** word.

Pick out the **naming** words and the **doing** words:

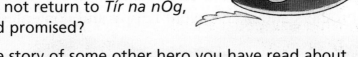

ground   looking   stone   riding

Write a sentence for each one.

Surf the Imagination

1 Draw a picture of the part of the story you liked best.

2 How do you think Niamh felt when Oisín did not return to *Tír na nÓg*, as he had promised?

3 Write the story of some other hero you have read about.

Mouse Search

1 Can you find some other stories about Oisín and the Fianna?

2 Gleann na Smól and Loch Léin are places in the story. What is the Irish name for where you live? Find out some other Irish place names.

The wheel monster

When Walter Rat was young, he lived with his own brothers and sisters, far away by a still pond in the misty mountains.

A little stream flowed into the pond and a little stream flowed out. The water was warm, and the pond was calm and green.

There were delicious reeds and rushes growing close to the banks, so there was always plenty for a water rat to eat. The ducks who shared the pond were friendly, and the fishes kept themselves to themselves like good neighbours should.

Nothing ever seemed to happen in the pond. Walter's brothers and sisters were happy and contented, but

Walter was full of questions.

'Where does the water come from?' he asked his big sister.

'It falls into the pond, and then it falls out again. Sometimes, it falls from the sky,' she replied.

'Water is always going somewhere!' said Walter, who loved to make jokes. 'When it falls out of the pond, where does it go?' he asked.

'I don't know. What tiresome questions you ask!' declared Walter's sister, and she swam away to eat the reeds and rushes.

'It's not important,' Walter's big brother told him.

'What if the place where it's going gets full up?' cried Walter Rat. 'That's very important!'

'The only important thing in life is reeds and rushes,' said Walter's brother, and he swam away to eat some more of them.

'Frogspawn!' Walter shouted, and went to talk to the ducks.

The ducks were silly creatures, but they had seen a lot of the world on their travels.

'The water goes down the hill to the shining sea,' the ducks told Walter Rat. 'The sea is very big and never gets full up.'

'Can you swim across the sea?' asked Walter.

The ducks quacked with laughter. 'We couldn't, but we don't have to. We can fly! Why don't you try!' They quacked again in their silly way.

'Frogspawn!' said Walter, who did not like jokes being made about himself. 'I'm a water rat and I'm going to swim across the sea. That's the only thing that will make me happy!'

At once, he swam down the stream that flowed out of the pond, calling 'Goodbye!' to his brother and sister, and to the ducks and fishes. He had set out on his Incredible Journey.

The stream ran strangely straight, with no reeds or rushes, and the water seemed to be flowing faster and faster. It was a wonder that it did not empty the pond, thought Walter Rat as he was swept along.

In the distance, he heard a clanking, clonking, swishing, sloshing sort of noise. It was a frightening noise, like no animal Walter had ever heard. It got closer, and closer.

Then a shadow cut out the sun and he saw the wheel monster! Its huge wheel thundered round and round, dripping water! It was chopping the stream into bits!

Walter Rat tried to climb out of the stream but the banks were stony walls, high and steep. He tried to turn back, but the dashing water sped him on, towards the wheel monster's fearsome clutches. Faster and faster he went, until — it was too late! The monster chopped the water with him in it, and carried him round, clunk, clonk! He was upside down and falling head over tail! He could not breathe!

Just when Walter Rat thought that he was going to drown, the wheel monster threw him out, swish, slosh! and he tumbled about in the foamy water until at last he bobbed the right way up.

Frogspawn! He had come right through the wheel monster's stomach, and out the other side! Thanking his lucky pondweed for being alive, Walter swam away as fast as his paws could carry him.

'That was how I lost my tail.'
Walter Rat proudly showed his
children the little stump where his
tail had been, and they touched it
with squeaks of excitement. Then
he carried on with his story.

From *The Incredible Journey of Walter Rat*
by Alan Browne, Hodder Children's Books

Blarney Blasts

1 How do you feel when your questions are not answered?

2 Imagine that you are one of Walter's sisters or brothers. What do you say when you discover that Walter has gone?

Log Jogging

This story reminds me of...

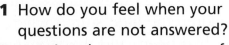

Tale and Detail

1 Where did the Rat family live?

2 What was the only thing that would make Walter happy?

3 When did Walter say goodbye to his brother and sister?

4 What did the wheel monster do?

5 Walter said a word over and over again. What was it?

Undercover Work

1 Why did Walter's sister not answer his questions?

2 What did Walter wonder about water?

3 How did Walter lose his tail?

4 Why did the pond never empty?

5 Why was Walter proud when he showed his children the stump of his tail?

6 Why do you think Walter left home?

Word Wizardry

Say the alphabet...

a b c d e f g h i j k l m n o p q r s t u v w x y z

animal, **b**rother and **c**reature are in alphabetical order because:

> **a**nimal begins with **a**
> **b**rother begins with **b**
> **c**reature begins with **c**

Keep going and put the words from the box below in alphabetical order.

rat	hill	frogspawn	girl
quacked	silly	pond	dog
tail	excitement	story	water

Surf the Imagination

1 Draw a picture of Walter Rat trying to get out of the water.
2 Imagine that you are Walter Rat.
   Write about how you felt when you lost your tail.
3 You have fallen into a fast-flowing river.
   Luckily, you are saved. Write about your adventure.

Mouse Search

1 What river or stream is near where you live?
   Find out what you can about it.
2 What creatures live in and on the banks of rivers and streams?
3 What happens when there is too much rain?

A magical mix-up

Marvello the magician had been invited to Mr McVicker's Zoo to perform some of his fabulous tricks at a children's birthday party. The very next day, something really strange happened to Cora the camel and Zena the zebra.

Everyone agreed that Cora was the most stuck-up animal in the Zoo. She never stopped boasting about her two magnificent humps.

'Of course I come from a noble family,' she would say in her snooty way. 'Really I'm far too high-class for a place like this.' Then she would wrinkle up her nose as if she were smelling something horrible.

46

Zena was just the opposite. She knew she had nothing at all to boast about. Some of her stripes were crooked and she was a little bit too fat. Still, she was always happy and full of fun — until the day after the party, that is.

It was all very sudden. One minute Zena was eating her dinner, and the next minute a sort of shivery feeling came over her. There was a thump! and something landed on her back. She snorted with fright and the other zebras stopped chewing to look around at her. Right in the middle of her back were two tiny humps. One had stripes going up and down, and the other had stripes going sideways.

'What is it?' squeaked Zena. 'What's happened to me?'

'It's a bit hard to explain,' stammered her brother Zack, hopping from one foot to another. 'There seem to be two kind of — um — humpy things on your back. Like two little footballs — sort of.'

Just then they heard a horrible yell of rage from the other end of the Zoo. Both Mr McVicker and Kenny stopped what they were doing and started running towards the noise. Kenny had been on his way to feed the seals, and was still carrying a bucket of fish. The fish were bouncing out of the bucket as he ran, leaving a trail all along the path behind him.

'Where's that dreadful noise coming from?' puffed Mr McVicker, hopping over the fish as he caught up with Kenny.

'Seems to be from the Camel House,' panted Kenny. 'Cora must be having a tantrum again.'

How right he was. Cora was kicking the walls inside the Camel House as hard as she could and bellowing, 'My beautiful, beautiful humps. Someone's stolen them. I always knew the other animals were jealous of me. Wait till I catch the thief!'

Kenny grabbed a bucket and banged it hard with a stick to stop her. Now they could see that her back was dead flat — as flat as his mother's ironing board, thought Kenny. He swallowed a grin. Better not let Cora see him laughing.

'Don't just stand there wasting time,' she roared. 'Go and find the thief at once.'

Mr McVicker and Kenny were only too glad to go. Outside the door they crashed into Mr Otis Owl, on his way to tell them about Zena.

'Great Galloping Glow-worms,' whispered Mr McVicker, turning pale. 'I knew there was something funny in the air today. Felt it the minute I got up. A sort of tingly feeling — like pins and needles.'

'If you ask me, that Marvello is to blame,' said Mr Otis. 'He used so much magic here yesterday that a tiny bit of it was bound to escape. It can make strange things happen. Like swopping Cora's humps over to Zena. Quite simple, really.'

Quite simple, was it? There was Zena sobbing at one end of the Zoo over two little stripey humps she didn't want, and Cora going mad at the other end because she hadn't any. How on earth could they sort out the mess?

Mr McVicker pulled himself together.

'Quick, Kenny, take the van down to Marvello's house. Bring him back immediately to unmagic Cora and Zena. Hurry, hurry!'

Kenny was back in ten minutes without Marvello.

'Bad news, boss,' he said. 'Marvello took the first plane to Lopsoland this morning. Gone to collect some new spells, his wife says. She lent me this,' and he showed Mr McVicker a big black book he was carrying. 'Mrs Marvello says it's her husband's book of spells, and we might find something in it to help.'

'Here, let me look,' offered Mr Otis. He put on his glasses and flipped through the pages with his wing. 'This looks like it. *"SPELL FOR PUTTING HUMPS BACK WHERE THEY BELONG."* I'll read it:

1. *Hold magic wand in right hand.*

2. *Stand on one leg with pineapple balanced on head.*

3. *Close eyes and say this spell: "Camels be humped and zebras be flat, Even a dunderhead should know that."*

4. *Wait for 5 seconds. Open eyes. The humps should then be back in the right place.'*

'Fine,' said Kenny. 'That sounds quite easy. I'll go and get a pineapple. You can do the rest, Mr Mac.'

More Fun at McVicker's Zoo by Mary Shiel, Children's Poolbeg

Blarney Blasts

1 Pretend that Mr McVicker sends an e-mail to Marvello in Lopsoland and forwards a copy to you. Tell your group what he says in the e-mail.

2 Talk to your partner about the biggest surprise (good or bad) that you have ever had.

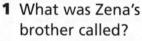

Log Jogging

As I read the story I felt...

Tale and Detail

1 What was Zena's brother called?
2 Who performed at the party?
3 Where did Marvello go?
4 Name the animals in the story.
5 What did Kenny bring from Marvello's house?

Undercover Work

1 Why do you think Kenny and Mr McVicker were amused by Cora?
2 Describe some tricks that magicians perform.
3 How is Cora's behaviour like Jane's in The walk (the first story in *Bright Sparks*)?
4 Why do camels have humps?
5 Cora and Zena were different. In what ways?

Word Wizardry

Write out these words in groups of three
so that the words in each group
have some connection.

Clue: The words magician, spell and wand make a group.

magician	food	patient
teacher	spell	menu
driver	pupil	bus
nurse	passenger	wand
cook	needle	homework

Surf the Imagination

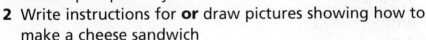

1 Make up a spell of your own.
2 Write instructions for **or** draw pictures showing how to
   make a cheese sandwich
   or
   put on a jumper.
3 Write an e-mail from Zena to her cousin telling about
   what happened to her.

Mouse Search

1 What food do these animals eat:
   seals, birds of prey, cats?
2 What is the difference between a
   zoo and a safari park?
3 Find out about some famous zoos.
4 Find out about Fota Island in Co Cork.

Harry Hedgehog

One sunny morning in autumn, Harry Hedgehog yawned and stretched.

Time to get up, he thought, rubbing the sleep from his eyes. He hopped out of bed and moved to the middle of the floor. Now for some hedgehog exercises, he thought.

He touched his toes three times from a standing position. 'That should be enough.'

Then he lay down on his front and began to do some press-ups, but he only managed four before collapsing in a heap! 'No need to strain myself!' Old Lepus, the wise old hare, had told him that exercise was good, especially in the morning.

Harry splashed cold water all over himself. 'Brrr! that's cold.' Then he shook himself like a dog, standing on one leg and shaking the other, then swapping positions. 'Completely dry,' he announced.

He looked at himself in the

mirror, checking his spines. There were leaves and bits of grass stuck to his back. 'Wow! What a messy back!' he thought.

Taking a brush he began to move it up and down his back. 'Aaah! That feels good.' Then he noticed a pile of spines on the floor.

'Oh no! I must have rubbed myself too hard. I'll be bald!'

He ran to the mirror again and checked his back carefully. Then he gave a sigh of relief.

'You'd never notice. Well, when you have over five thousand spines, losing a few here and there should make no difference.'

Not that he'd ever counted his spines. It was Old Lepus who'd told him how many spines he had, and *he* knew everything — well, almost everything.

Harry put on his waistcoat. This was a gift from the old hare and it certainly helped keep his back fairly clear of grasses and leaves, and kept him warm on these chilly autumn mornings.

Harry was ready to face the day.

'Boy, I'm hungry,' he said. 'What can I find for breakfast?' He searched the cupboard. 'Empty! Oh no!' Then, looking out the window at the leaves dancing in the wind, he thought: 'Ah yes! That's it! I'll visit the old orchard. There's sure to be lots to eat there!' His mouth watered just thinking about all those juicy apples and pears.

He set off. The day was very blustery, and a sycamore leaf flew straight into his face and another onto his head.

'Do you mind!' he said to the wind. 'I've just brushed my spines!' Another one stuck to his bottom.

'Oh bother! At least there will be shelter in
the orchard.'

'Hello, Harry,' called a voice from behind him.
Harry looked around to see his good friend Renny Fox
padding up the woodland path. 'Windy, isn't it!'
said Renny.

'Oh yes,' said Harry, feeling the chill. 'It's what my
uncle calls a *lazy* wind.'

The fox looked blankly at Harry. 'Lazy?'

'You see,' explained Harry, 'it would rather go through
you than go around you!'

Renny laughed loudly. 'That's a good one! I must tell it

to my cousins. I'm off to visit them tomorrow. They live near the mountains. It's my Uncle Redcote's birthday and there's a party. You know, they live near a wishing well.'

'Really!' said Harry. 'Does it work?'

'Well, my uncle believes it does. He told me about the time his brother had his brush shot off completely by an angry farmer. He made a wish by the well and the very next day he grew a fine new bushy tail!'

'Amazing!' said Harry. 'I remember once making a wish when I saw a shooting star.'

'And did it come true?' asked Renny.

'I don't know,' said Harry.

'What do you mean, you don't know?'

'Well, I couldn't remember what I'd wished for!'

Renny laughed, and looked up at the swallows gathering on the wires preparing for their long flight to

Africa. 'Did you ever wish you could fly? It would be nice, wouldn't it?'

'Why don't you make a wish at the wishing well for the power of flight?' said Harry.

'I might just do that.'

Another leaf landed on Harry's head.

'Oh, I just remembered. I'm on my way to the old orchard. Do you want to come?'

'Great idea!' said Renny.

'Let's go!'

The Bat Who Was All in a Flap! by Don Conroy,
The O'Brien Press Ltd

Blarney Blasts

 1 Has anything ever made you sigh with relief? Tell about it.

 2 When you are alone and feeling hungry, what do you do?

Log Jogging

Look at your Log Jogging list on page 192.

Pick one suggestion and write about it.

Tale and Detail

1 At what time of the year is this story set?

2 Who had given Harry the waistcoat?

3 What was Harry going to have for breakfast?

4 How did Harry describe the wind?

5 What was the great idea that Harry had?

Undercover Work

1 In your opinion, why was the farmer angry with the fox?

2 Why did Renny think it was a good idea to go to the orchard?

3 What sentences in the story tell us that it is Autumn?

4 What type of animal is Uncle Redcote?

5 In what ways did the wise old hare show that he cared for Harry?

6 In stories you have read or films you have watched, what clothes have animals worn?

60

Word Wizardry

Match each word on the left with the word
or words that are closest in meaning
on the right.

waistcoat	changing
sycamore	exercise
brush	fox's tail
press-ups	garment
collapsing	a tree
swapping	falling down

Surf the Imagination

1 Imagine that you are an animal.
What type of animal are you?
What do you like and dislike about
being this animal?
Draw a picture of yourself.
2 Renny Fox invited Harry Hedgehog to
the birthday party. Write the story of
what happened at the party.

Mouse Search

1 Find out why exercise is good
for you.
2 Find out why farmers do not
like foxes.
3 Do you know any stories that
have talking animals?
Write about one.

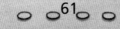

61

Save our sweetshop

This story happened a long time ago when pocket money meant pennies and sixpences that would buy you enough sweets to last ages. There were real sweetshops then. I don't mean shops that sell ordinary things as well, like bread and sausages. Real sweetshops sell nothing but sweets — the kind of shop that every child dreams of owning some day. And there was one just like that around the corner from Barrow Street where I lived. By the way, my name is Brendan, although everyone calls me Benny.

The shop was old and a bit lopsided as if it were leaning on the house beside it for support. A sign over the green door said THE NOOK, in flaking red letters. The people who owned the shop were called Nancy and Dolly. They lived there too, and you could smell their dinner cooking in the kitchen at the back. A bell went 'Ding!' when you went in

PENNY TRAY
SELECTION

so they knew they had a customer, and one of them
would come in through a door behind the counter.
We always hoped it was Dolly. Dolly was the nice one;
she smiled and said hello and her three jolly chins
wobbled when she laughed. She was always chewing,
because she loved sweets as much as we did.

'These are very nice,' she'd say, whenever she got any
new ones. Or, 'I'm not too sure about these,' and she'd
let us sample them to see what we thought. 'The proof
of the pudding is in the eating,' she'd say.

Nancy was sour and skinny. She always looked as if she had just tasted something horrible. She drummed her fingers on the counter when we were trying to make up our minds about what we wanted.

'Tsk, tsk, I've a good mind to give up selling sweets altogether,' she'd say, her tongue clicking impatiently. 'It's more trouble than it's worth.'

The Nook had a huge selection of the most scrumptious sweets you could imagine: jars and jars of Gobstoppers, Aniseed Balls and Peppermint Creams,

Pear Drops that tasted like nail varnish and Cough-No-Mores that tasted like medicine, Dolly Mixtures and Bull's-eyes, Jelly Babies, Mint Humbugs and Acid Drops, Bonbons and Chocolate Satins. And they were just the penny sweets! There was slab toffee in a tray, with a little silver hammer for breaking it into pieces, Liquorice Laces and Pipes, Sugar Mice, Peggy's Legs, Sherbet Dabs and Suckers and huge pink Lucky Lumps that didn't really taste very nice but in which you might find money if you were lucky.

It was the best sweetshop in town and us kids from Barrow Street raced down there every Saturday to spend our pocket money.

So you can imagine our dismay one Saturday when we saw a sign on the door that said:

WE REGRET TO INFORM OUR
CUSTOMERS THAT THE NOOK
WILL BE CLOSING IN A FORTNIGHT.
WE WOULD LIKE TO THANK
EVERYBODY FOR THEIR
SUPPORT OVER THE YEARS.

'I'll bet this is all Nancy's idea,' Frankie said, scowling.

'It's more trouble than it's worth,' Rita said, mimicking Nancy's rasping voice.

Denis began to sniffle. 'Now we'll have no more sweets,' he whimpered.

'Quit blubbing!' Frankie said, nudging him with his elbow.

Denis was Frankie's younger brother. He always tagged along because Frankie's mam made him bring Denis everywhere.

Dolly was behind the counter cutting up newspaper to make the cones that were used instead of bags for the sweets.

'I don't suppose I'll be needing too many of these in the time that's left,' she said. 'But doing something keeps my mind off things.'

'So it's true then?' Rita asked. 'The shop is closing for ever?'

'I'm afraid so,' Dolly said. 'The council says the building is unsafe. It will have to be demolished if we don't repair it and that would cost a lot more money than we have.'

'They can't do that!' Rita said indignantly, flicking her plaits back. 'This is the best sweetshop in town!'

Dolly smiled. She picked up the little silver hammer.

'This hammer has cracked more toffee than I've had hot dinners,' she said softly. She sighed and popped a Bonbon into her mouth.

'And more children have rotted the teeth out of their heads from eating more sweets than is good for them!' Nancy snapped as she came in the door. 'Still, I wasn't ready to retire yet. And I gave that young whippersnapper from the council a piece of my mind, I can tell you!'

'Can't you do anything about it?' Rita asked.

'Like what?' Nancy spluttered. 'Nothing short of a miracle will keep this place open!'

Dolly stifled a sob and disappeared into the back of the shop.

'Now, if you lot can make up your minds quickly, you can leave us to spend our last few days here in peace!' Nancy said, her fingers drumming rapidly on the counter.

Save our Sweetshop by Lorraine Francis, Poolbeg Press

Blarney Blasts

1 Dolly and Nancy are asked to speak on a television chat show about their years in the shop. Act out what happens.

2 Have a discussion between the people who think the sweetshop should close and the people who think it should stay open.

Log Jogging

Look at your Log Jogging list on page 192.

Pick one suggestion and write about it.

Tale and Detail

1 Name the children in the story.

2 What were used instead of bags for the sweets?

3 Where did the children in the story live?

4 How long is a fortnight?

5 Who had the habit of drumming her fingers on the counter?

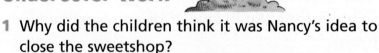

Undercover Work

1 Why did the children think it was Nancy's idea to close the sweetshop?

2 What kind of voice did Nancy have?

3 What did Dolly mean when she said:

'This hammer has cracked more toffee than I've had hot dinners'?

4 What did Nancy mean when she said:

'I gave that young whippersnapper from the council a piece of my mind'?

5 The two sisters, Dolly and Nancy, were very different from each other. How do we know this?

Word Wizardry

Some words are used to tell us about people and things.
For example, Dolly and Nancy are described in the story.

Which words from the list are
used to describe Dolly and which
are used to describe Nancy?
Can you think of other words to
describe each of them?

friendly	cross
kind	generous
impatient	sour
skinny	nice

Dolly	Nancy

Surf the Imagination

1 Imagine that you own a shop. Draw a picture of it.
2 Make a sign for the front of your shop.
3 Write about your favourite shop.

Mouse Search

1 Many years ago there were no supermarkets.
  Ask your parents and grandparents to tell you about the
  shops when they were young.
2 Most sweets have a lot of sugar in them. Find out how
  sugar rots your teeth. What can you do to keep your teeth
  healthy, even if you eat sugary foods?

Foolish brothers

On a small farm in the west of Ireland, there lived two brothers, Mick and Seán. They had a cow and one horse and a little vegetable garden at the edge of the woods. Their farm provided them with plenty of food and a small income, but they were never happy with what they had, and always longed for more.

One day, when they were working in their garden, they heard a shout coming from the woods. It was a very screechy sort of a shout; they didn't know if it was an animal or person who had made it. They went to investigate and as they walked into the woods, they saw a little small man pinned to the ground under a branch that had fallen down, right on top of him!

This little fellow was wearing a suit of bottle green and beside him there was a little hammer and some tiny shoes. He was calling out for someone to set him free. Mick was about to pick up the branch but Seán grabbed him by the arm.

'Will you wait a minute, Mick, can't you see that this is a leprechaun that we've found. Look, there is a little hammer beside him and the little fairy shoes.

70

Sure everybody knows that a leprechaun is the fairy
shoe-maker and he can give us three wishes.'

They told the leprechaun that they would set him free
if he promised to give them the wishes.

'I will not give ye my wishes,' said the leprechaun,
'they're the only ones I have'.

Well Mick and Seán told him they just wouldn't set him
free unless he gave them the wishes and finally the little
man had to give in. But he warned them, 'these wishes
will make you no better off than you were before you
had them'.

The brothers didn't care about that and as long as they
had the promise of the wishes, they were satisfied.
They picked up the branch and, in a flash,
the leprechaun vanished.

Mick and Seán started to walk back toward their little cottage and they were wondering what great things they were going to wish for. Oh a great big farm of land with a nice big house and hundreds of cattle. Their minds were filled with these thoughts as they walked in the door to their kitchen.

'Now Mick, we should sit down first and have our supper and then we'll decide what we are going to wish for,' Seán said.

'Oh I suppose you're right,' says Mick, 'but I wish we had a pot of soup on the fire right now so we could have the supper and get it over with'.

Well these words were no sooner out of Mick's mouth when a pot of soup appeared on the fire!

Oh Seán was in a terrible rage.

'Look what you did, you silly thing, you wasted one of our good wishes on an old pot of soup. Oh you were so silly I wish that pot of soup would stick on to your nose!'

These words were no sooner out of Seán's mouth when that pot of soup came up from the fire and stuck on to Mick's nose! Well, they pulled at it and they tugged at it, but no matter what they did, that pot of soup would not budge. Seán was beginning to realise that they had only one wish left and was wondering how they could possibly use it for something useful, so he says to Mick, 'do you know Mick, I think you look very handsome with the pot of soup on your nose. Do you think maybe you could live like that so we could use the last wish on something constructive and useful?'

Mick finally convinced Seán that he could not spend the rest of his life with a pot of soup stuck to his nose, so they had to use the last wish to get rid of it. As soon as they wished that the pot of soup be gone, it was gone. And with it went the three wishes.

So the leprechaun was right; they were no better off after they got those wishes than they were before they had them.

Foolish Brothers by Bairbre McCarthy, Mercier Press

Blarney Blasts

C 1 Imagine you are a local television reporter who saw Mick with the pot of soup on his nose.
What would you say on television?

G 2 The leprechaun reports the theft of his three wishes to the gardaí.
Act out the conversation between the leprechaun and the gardaí.

Log Jogging

Look at your Log Jogging list on page 192.
Pick one suggestion and write about it.

Tale and Detail

1 Where did the brothers find the leprechaun?
2 Why did the leprechaun not want to give away his wishes?
3 What warning did the leprechaun give to the brothers?
4 How was the first wish used?
5 How did Seán try to convince Mick to keep the pot of soup on his nose?

Undercover Work

1 Why did the brothers not care about the leprechaun's warning?
2 What does the story tell us about the brothers?
3 If Mick and Seán ever found another leprechaun, what do you think they would do?
4 What would have happened if the leprechaun had not given his wishes to Mick and Seán?

Word Wizardry

Can you find the following words in the wordsearch?

I   you   he   she   it   we   they

s	x	i	v	i	h
y	z	s	b	t	e
o	v	h	e	e	w
u	u	e	l	m	e
t	h	e	y	e	x
m	e	q	l	p	z

Surf the Imagination

1 Write about three things that you wish for.
2 Mick looked silly with the pot of soup on his nose.
Draw some pictures of other things which would look silly.

Mouse Search

1 Look in your atlas at the map of Ireland.
Find the names of three counties in the West.
2 What ingredients are used to make soup?
Write your own soup recipe.

Emily's legs

To begin with, nobody noticed.

Mind you, you couldn't blame Mother Spider. If she'd only had one baby, she'd have been sure to notice.

But she had a hundred babies, all hatching out at the same time. How could she be expected to know that ninety-nine spiderlings were normal and one was different?

Father Spider didn't notice. For one thing, he didn't like children.

For another, he was always too busy sitting quite still, waiting for house-flies and bluebottles to land in his web, in the highest darkest corner of the room.

Emily's ninety-nine brothers and sisters didn't notice.

Nobody noticed, not even Emily, until the night of the Spider Sports.

For the grown-up spiders, there were lots of different events. There was web-spinning (how quickly could you make a whole one from start to finish) and fly-parcelling (how quickly could you tie up a fly in silken threads) and fly-eating (how quickly could you… yes, well, I needn't explain that.

And there was abseiling, where you let out a thread and whizzed down it from the ceiling,

and thread-climbing,
where you whizzed
back up again.

But for the spiderlings
there were only the
eight-legged races.

Now this was where
Emily's troubles began.

Not that she didn't
run in the eight-legged
races at the Spider
Sports.

She did.

Not that she didn't win.
She did.

The trouble was that
she won them all and
she won them all so
easily.

First, all the
spiderlings were lined
up at one end of the
room, and they had to
race across the carpet to
the other end.

Emily won easily.

Then they had to race
up the wall of the
room.

Emily won easily.

Then they had to race
down the wall.

Emily won easily.

Last of all was the upside-down eight-legged race, right across the ceiling.

Yes, you've guessed, Emily won easily.

'Amazing!' said all the grown-up spiders. 'Well done, Emily!'

But the spiderlings weren't so happy.

'Why does Emily *always* win?' they asked one another.

'Why does Emily *always* win?' they asked the grown-up spiders.

'Because she's the fastest, of course,' said the grown-up spiders in the knowing way that old folk have.

'But *why* is she the fastest?' asked the spiderlings in the annoying way that young folk have. And that was when the truth was discovered.

Emily was asked to appear in front of the Spider Sports Committee to receive her prizes, four neatly parcelled little flies.

'Congratulations, Emily,' said the chairperson of the

78

Sports Committee. 'You have won all four eight-legged races. Why is that, do you think?'

'If you please,' said Emily (for she was by nature a polite spiderling), 'it's because I ran the fastest'.

'Ah!' said a very old grown-up spider. 'But *why* did you run the fastest?'

Emily scratched her head with her two front legs. 'I don't really know,' she said modestly. 'I suppose I just legged it quicker than they did.'

'Legged it?' said the very old grown-up spider.

'Legged it?' said all the other grown-up spiders.

And they all looked carefully at Emily's legs.

They weren't any different from the legs of all the other spiderlings. They were no longer. They were no stronger. They were no hairier. But suddenly they all saw that, though Emily was scratching her head with her two front legs, yet she was still standing on eight others.

Emily had ten legs!

Emily's Legs by Dick King-Smith, Macdonald Young Books

Blarney Blasts

1 You are the chairperson of the Sports Committee and are speaking on the evening news about Emily's ten legs. What would you say?

2 What do you remember about your last sports day? Tell your partner about it.

Log Jogging

Look at your Log Jogging list on page 192.

Pick one suggestion and write about it.

Tale and Detail

1 How many baby spiders are in the story?
2 At what time of day did the Spider Sports take place?
3 Who won all the races?
4 What prizes did Emily get?
5 True or false? Emily had twelve legs.

Undercover Work

1 How did father spider feel about children? Suggest why.

2 Why did the Spider Sports take place at night time?
3 How was Emily able to travel so fast?
4 What did the spiderling do that led to the discovery?
5 Did Emily cheat? Explain what you think.

Word Wizardry

Use your dictionary to find the following words. It will tell you what the parent is called. Write the name of each parent.

chick	_____	kitten	_____
duckling	_____	lamb	_____
foal	_____	piglet	_____
kid	_____	pup	_____

Surf the Imagination

Write a description of an insect (examine the insect itself or a picture of one).

Mouse Search

1 Find out about your favourite sporting hero. Write a story or make a scrapbook of the information.
2 Write the names and a short description of five insects. Illustrate or copy them if you can.

Santa Claus

Henry, Sam and Mr Fielding are three mice who decide to travel together in search of adventure. They meet many other creatures on their travels and have many narrow escapes. They end up at Mr Fielding's uncle's house where they spend Christmas. While out for a walk on Christmas Eve, they hide in a tree, only to find it is cut down and taken to a strange house from where escape seems impossible. Imagine their surprise when a visitor arrives down the chimney and takes them on their best adventure yet.

At last the house grew silent as everyone had gone to bed. Over the mantelpiece hung two red stockings, and on a little table by the fireplace was a plate with a mince pie and a glass of milk.

'I wonder who those are for?' said Mr Fielding, as the three mice climbed down from the tree. 'I feel a bit peckish.'

'Never mind about food,' snapped Sam. 'We must get out of here.'

'Yes,' wailed Henry, 'there is no time to lose'.

The mice ran this way and that, trying to get out of the room, but it was no use. The door was shut tight. The window was shut tight. There was just no way out.

'Whatever shall we do?' asked Mr Fielding. 'I don't want to be hung on that tree. It would be most uncomfortable.'

'I want to spend Christmas at the Bigger house,' sobbed Henry, and he thought of all the presents under the tree and the food in the kitchen and he sobbed louder than ever.

'Stop crying,' said Sam crossly.

'What a tiresome fellow he is,' thought Mr Fielding. 'Always weeping and wailing.'

After a while the three mice stopped running here and there as they were quite tired out. Suddenly they heard a noise, a sort of tinkling, jingling noise and it seemed to be coming from right up inside the chimney. Then there came a bump and then another one.

'Someone is coming down the chimney!' said Sam, and the three mice ran in alarm up the tree again.

'Bang, bump, bump,' went the noise, and what should the mice see as they peeped out from the branches but a large black boot, and then another one, coming out of the chimney. Next came a long red coat, followed by a face with a white beard and a red cap.

'Good gracious me,' whispered Sam. 'It's Santa Claus!'
— and so it was, as large as life and a little sooty from
his climb down the chimney. Over his shoulder he
carried a sack. He puffed and panted as he put it down
on the floor, for it was a very full sack and heavy.

Suddenly Sam cried, 'We'll ask Santa to save us!'

'What a splendid idea!' said Henry and Mr Fielding
together and the three mice scampered down the tree.

What a surprise Santa Claus got when the mice
suddenly hurtled from the branches of the Christmas tree
and landed right at his feet.

'Bless my beard and
whiskers,' said Santa.
'Where have *you* come from?'

Then the three mice told him
what had happened. 'Will you
please get us out of here?'
asked Mr Fielding.

'Yes, please do,' wailed Henry, 'for we want to spend
Christmas at the Bigger house'. And he started to turn
the tears on again until Sam stopped him with a glare.

'Well,' said Santa Claus, 'I have a busy night ahead of
me and a long way to travel, but I might just be able to
do that for you if you do something to help me'.

'Anything, anything!' cried the mice.

'Well, it's like this,' said Santa. 'One of my reindeers is
a restless fellow and a bit full of mischief, and sometimes
he just won't stand still while I make my deliveries.
He stamps and snorts on the roof tops and makes an awful
noise. He will waken all the children if I am not careful,
and that just wouldn't do. You mice could chat to him
while I get on with my work. You know — keep his
mind busy and his feet still.'

'Yes, yes, we will do that!' said Sam.

'Certainly, certainly!' said Mr Fielding.

'Anything, anything!' said Henry. 'Just get us out of here.'

And so the three mice spent a busy and exciting night, but first Santa Claus filled the two red stockings over the mantelpiece with toys, and then he ate the mince pie and drank the milk on the little table. He even put three clockwork mice in the branches of the Christmas tree so that the two children wouldn't be disappointed when they found the real mice gone.

The mice were in a fever to be off and it seemed as if Santa would never be ready, but a loud banging on the roof made him hurry.

'Quick!' he said to the mice. 'Climb into my sack and we'll be off before that reindeer wakens everyone.'

Up, up the chimney Santa climbed with the mice and out on to the snowy roof among the stars, and what a sight met the eyes of the tree mice!

There on the roof top were four beautiful reindeers pulling a big shiny red sleigh piled high with toys.

Their coats were like velvet in the moonlight, for they had been groomed and prepared for many months for this special night. They wore green harness on which shone and tinkled dozens of little silver bells.

'Climb in,' said Santa Claus, and he tucked the mice up in warm rugs for the night was very cold. 'Giddy up there,' he called, flicking his long whip, and with a toss of their beautiful heads, horns flashing in the moonlight, silver bells ringing, the four reindeers leaped forward. Off the roof top and out into the night they galloped among the stars. Never had the mice had such an adventure.

The Adventures of Henry and Sam and Mr Fielding
by Vera Pettigrew, The Children's Press

The three mice help Santa Claus to deliver toys to children all over the world. Find out what happens and how the mice decide to return to their own homes by reading *The Adventures of Henry and Sam and Mr Fielding* by Vera Pettigrew, The Children's Press.

Blarney Blasts

1 When Christmas Day comes, the reindeer return to the North Pole. One of the deer tells his friends about the three mice and the adventure they had. Tell a partner what you think he says.

2 Pretend you are Santa delivering the toys. Tell the mice what you have for the two children.

Log Jogging

Look at your Log Jogging list on page 192.

Pick one suggestion and write about it.

Tale and Detail

1 Why could the mice not get out of the room?
2 How did Santa Claus get into the house?
3 In what way could the mice help Santa Claus?
4 Describe what the mice saw on the roof.
5 What did Santa do for the mice when they climbed in?

Undercover Work

1 How many children lived in the house? How do you know?
2 In your opinion, why did Henry cry?
3 Why was Santa Claus concerned about the children waking up?
4 Santa ate mince pies. What other foods do we eat at Christmas?
5 Where might the children look for the mice?

Word Wizardry

Capital letters always start a sentence and come after a **full stop**.
Put in the capital letters in the paragraph below.

the mice spent a busy and exciting night. first Santa Claus filled the two red stockings with toys. he put them back over the mantelpiece. he ate the mince pies and drank the milk. then he put three clockwork mice on the tree. sam was pleased to be going with Santa. Mr Fielding led the way into Santa's sack. up the chimney Santa climbed. they all got into the sleigh.

Surf the Imagination

1 Imagine that you are one of the mice. Write what happened after you set off in Santa's sleigh. Give each of the reindeer a name.
2 One of the reindeer sends a postcard home from where you live. Design the postcard and show what the reindeer has written.
3 Santa decides to give the mice a job. What do they have to do?
4 Write a Christmas poem.

Mouse Search

1 Find out about Christmas customs around the world. If possible use the Internet.
2 Make a list of all the Christmas songs people in your class know.

89

Three fables

The rabbit and the turtle

One day a rabbit was making fun of a turtle for being so slow. 'Wait a bit,' said the turtle. 'I'll run a race with you and I'll bet that I win.' 'Oh, well,' replied the rabbit, who was much amused by the idea, 'let's try and see'. They agreed that the fox should set a course for them

90

and be the judge. When the time came, both started out together, but the rabbit was soon so far ahead that he thought he might as well have a little rest. Down he lay

and fell fast asleep. Meanwhile the turtle kept plodding on and finally reached the goal. At last the rabbit woke up with a start, and dashed on as fast as he could, only to find that the turtle had already won the race.

Slow and steady wins the race.

The fox and the goat

One day a fox fell down a well and could not scramble out again. The water was not very deep but the sides of the well were smooth and covered in slippery moss so that every time the fox struggled up a few inches, he slipped down again with a splash into the water.

After some time a goat came along and peered curiously over the edge.

'What are you doing down there, fox?' he asked.

The fox saw his chance to escape.

'Are you quite alone?' he asked mysteriously. 'I don't want everyone to come at once. But the water in this well is so good that I just cannot stop drinking it. Come on in and try it. You'll see it is better than anything you ever tasted before.'

Without thinking twice, the goat jumped in and began to drink eagerly. After a while he had had enough to drink and he looked round to see how he could get out.

'No problem at all, my dear fellow,' said the fox. 'You stand on your hind legs and I'll climb on your back. If I balance on your horns I'll just about reach the ground. Then I'll lean over and pull you up after me.'

So the goat stood on his hind legs and the fox climbed quickly out of the well. Trotting off across the fields, he called out to the goat:

'If you had as much sense in your head as you have hairs in your beard, my friend, you would have made sure you could get out of that well before ever you jumped in.'

Look before you leap.

The dog and the bone

A dog once stole a bone from a butcher's shop. He ran off down the street as fast as he could, across the village green and down the hill to a rough bridge over a stream. There he paused, panting, to look at the clear, clean water.

He gave a start. Looking up at him from the water was another dog. The other dog was holding a big, juicy bone in its mouth. The first dog glared at the second dog and the second dog glared fiercely back at him.

The first dog's mouth began to water.

'If I had that bone,' he thought greedily, 'I could

eat it now and save mine for later. I know just the place to bury it. Besides, that bone looks better than mine. It has more meat on it.'

The first dog growled threateningly — and the dog in the water bared its teeth and seemed to growl back at him.

'So you want a fight, do you?' growled the first dog, and he opened his mouth to grab the second dog's bone.

Splash! The first dog's bone fell into the stream and was swept away by the current. Barking angrily, he leaned forward to attack, but as his bone fell into the water, the second dog seemed to vanish away. Its bone vanished with it. As the ripples gradually smoothed away, the dog was left feeling rather foolish — and very hungry — staring at his own reflection.

Be satisfied with what you have.

Blarney Blasts

1 The turtle and the dog meet the goat one afternoon.
   They plan to get revenge on the fox.
   Discuss their plan with a partner and how it will work.

2 You and your friends meet the fox.
   You question him about the way he treats others.
   What do you ask him and how does he answer?

3 In a group, talk about a time when you did something without thinking first. What happened?

Log Jogging

Look at your Log Jogging list on page 192.

Pick one suggestion and write about it.

Tale and Detail

Make questions for these answers:

1 The turtle won the race.
2 Slow and steady wins the race.
3 The sides of the well were covered with slippery moss.
4 He fooled the goat.
5 Look before you leap.
6 He felt very foolish and very hungry.
7 Be satisfied with what you have.

Undercover Work

1 Why do you think animals are used instead of people in the fables?

2 Do you think the rabbit, the goat and the dog deserved what happened to them?

3 The moral of each fable is given at the end. Explain one moral in your own words and give an example to show you understand it.

4 Would you ever disagree with the morals in these stories?

Word Wizardry

Choose the correct word from the box below to complete the sentences.

| ice | an ox | sugar | a mountain | gold |

The water was as cold as _____

The giant was as strong as _____

The dinosaur was as big as _____

The child was as good as _____

The bun was as sweet as _____

Surf the Imagination

1 Draw a picture story of one of these fables.
2 Write your own fable, using animals that you know. Read your fable to others in your class.

Mouse Search

1 Choose one of the animals in the Three fables. Find out what you can about this animal.
2 In your home you get water from taps. Find out how water gets to your home.
3 How did people get water before houses had indoor plumbing?
4 A desert has very little water. Use your atlas to find three places where there are deserts.

Dark is exciting

Plop was a baby Barn Owl, and he
lived with his Mummy and Daddy at
the top of a very tall tree in a field.

Plop was fat and fluffy.

He had a beautiful heart-shaped ruff.

He had enormous, round eyes.

He had very knackety knees.

In fact he was exactly the same as
every baby Barn Owl that has ever
been — except for one thing.

99

Plop was afraid of the dark.

'You *can't* be afraid of the dark,' said his Mummy. 'Owls are *never* afraid of the dark.'

'This one is,' Plop said.

'But owls are *night* birds,' she said.

Plop looked down at his toes. 'I don't want to be a night bird,' he mumbled. 'I want to be a day bird.'

'You *are* what you *are*,' said Mrs Barn Owl firmly.

'Yes, I know,' agreed Plop, 'and what I are is afraid of the dark'.

'Oh dear,' said Mrs Barn Owl. It was clear that she was going to need a lot of patience. She shut her eyes and tried to think how best she could help Plop not to be afraid. Plop waited.

His mother opened her eyes again. 'Plop, you are only afraid of the dark because you don't know about it. What *do* you know about the dark?'

'It's black,' said Plop.

'Well, that's wrong for a start. It can be silver or blue or grey or lots of other colours, but almost never black. What else do you know about it?'

'I don't like it,' said Plop. 'I do not like it AT ALL.'

'That's not *knowing* something,' said his mother. 'That's *feeling* something. I don't think you know anything about the dark at all.'

'Dark is nasty,' Plop said loudly.

'You don't know that. You have never had your beak outside the nest-hole after dusk. I think you had better go down into the world and find out a lot more about the dark before you make up your mind about it.'

'Now?' said Plop.

'Now,' said his mother.

Plop climbed out of the nest-hole and wobbled along the branch outside. He peeped over the edge. The world seemed to be a very long way down.

'I'm not a very good lander,' he said. 'I might spill myself.'

'Your landing will improve with practice,' said his mother. 'Look! There's a little boy down there on the edge of the wood collecting sticks. Go and talk to him about it.'

'Now?' said Plop.

'Now,' said his mother. So Plop shut his eyes, took a deep breath, and fell off his branch.

His small white wings carried him down, but, as he said, he was not a good lander. He did seven very fast somersaults past the little boy.

'Ooh!' cried the little boy. 'A giant Catherine-wheel!'

'Actually,' said the Catherine-wheel, picking himself up, 'I'm a Barn Owl'.

'Oh yes — so you are,' said the little boy with obvious disappointment. 'Of course, you couldn't be a firework yet. Dad says we can't have the fireworks until it gets dark. Oh, I wish it would hurry up and get dark *soon*.'

'You *want* it to get dark?' said Plop in amazement.

'Oh, YES,' said the little boy. 'DARK IS EXCITING. And tonight is specially exciting because we're going to have fireworks.'

'What are fireworks?' asked Plop. 'I don't think owls have them — not Barn Owls, anyway.'

'Don't you?' said the little boy. 'Oh, you poor thing. Well, there are rockets, and flying saucers, and volcanoes, and golden rain, and sparklers, and ...'

'But what *are* they?' begged Plop. 'Do you eat them?'

'NO!' laughed the little boy. 'Daddy sets fire to their tails and they *whoosh* into the air and fill the sky with coloured stars — well, the rockets, that is. I'm allowed to hold the sparklers.'

'What about the volcanoes? And the golden rain? What do they do?'

'Oh, they sort of burst into showers of stars. The golden rain *pours* — well, like rain.'

'And the flying saucers?'

'Oh, they're super! They whizz round your head and make a sort of *wheeee* noise. I like them best.'

'I think I would like fireworks,' said Plop.

'I'm sure you would,' the little boy said. 'Look here, where do you live?'

'Up in that tree — in the top flat. There are squirrels farther down.'

'That big tree in the middle of the field? Well, you can watch our fireworks from there! That's our garden — the one with the swing. You look out as soon as it gets dark ...'

'Does it *have* to be dark?' asked Plop.

'Of course it does! You can't see fireworks unless it's dark. Well, I must go. These sticks are for the bonfire.'

'Bonfire?' said Plop. 'What's that?'

'You'll see if you look out tonight. Goodbye!'

'Goodbye,' said Plop, bobbing up and down in a funny little bow.

103

He watched the boy run across the field, and then took a little run himself, spread his wings, and fluttered up to the landing branch. He slithered along it on his tummy and dived head first into the nest-hole.

'Well?' said his mother.

'The little boy says DARK IS EXCITING.'

'And what do you think, Plop?'

'I still do not like it AT ALL,' said Plop, 'but I'm going to watch the fireworks — if you will sit by me'.

'I will sit by you,' said his mother.

'So will I,' said his father, who had just woken up. 'I like fireworks.'

So that is what they did.

When it began to get dark, Plop waddled to the mouth of the nest-hole and peered out cautiously.

'Come on, Plop! I think they're starting,' called Mr Barn Owl. He was already in position on a big branch at the very top of the tree. 'We shall see beautifully from here.'

Plop took two brave little steps out of the nest-hole.
'I'm here,' said his mother quietly. 'Come on.'

So together, wings almost touching, they flew up to join Mr Barn Owl.

They were only just in time. There were flames leaping and crackling at the end of the little boy's garden. 'That must be the bonfire!' squeaked Plop.

Hardly had Plop got his wings tucked away, when 'WHOOSH!' — up went a rocket and spat out a shower of green stars. 'Ooooh!' said Plop, his eyes like saucers.

A fountain of dancing stars sprang up from the ground — and another and another. 'Ooooh!' said Plop again.

'You sound like a tawny owl,' said his father. 'Goodness! What's that?'

Something was whizzing about leaving bright trails of squiggles behind it and making a loud 'Wheeee!' noise.

105

'Oh, that's a flying saucer,' said Plop.

'Really?' his father said. 'I've never seen one of those before. You seem to know all about it. What's that fizzy one that keeps jigging up and down?'

'I expect that's my friend with a sparkler. Oooooh! There's a me!'

'I beg your pardon?' said Plop's father.

'It's a Catherine-wheel! The little boy thought I was a Catherine-wheel when

I landed. Oh, isn't it beautiful?
And he thought *I* was one!'

Mr Barn Owl watched the whirling,
sparking circles spinning round and
round.

'That must have been quite a landing!'
he said.

The Owl who was Afraid of the Dark
by Jill Tomlinson, Egmont

107

Blarney Blasts

1 When Plop meets his cousins, he tells them about the night he watched the fireworks.
What did he say? Tell a partner.

2 Talk about something you don't like to a group. Listen to them as they tell you about their dislikes.

Log Jogging

Look at your Log Jogging list on page 192.

Pick one suggestion and write about it.

Tale and Detail

1 Where did Plop live?
2 Why did Plop want to be a day bird?
3 How did Plop's mum explain his fear of the dark?
4 Who was the first person to speak to Plop after the seven somersaults?
5 List three types of fireworks in the story.

Undercover Work

1 How did Mammy try to put Plop's mind at rest?
2 Why are people sometimes called night owls?
3 Why did Plop want his parents to sit with him when he watched the fireworks?
4 Why did Plop's dad say 'That must have been quite a landing'?
5 Describe the ways the grown-up owls encouraged Plop to become less afraid of the dark.

Word Wizardry

Use the words in the box to fill in
the gaps in the paragraph.

| he | his | she | her |

Plop lived with _____ Mummy and Daddy. _____ had

enormous round eyes and a beautiful, heart-shaped ruff.

There was one problem. _____ was afraid of the dark.

Mrs Barn Owl shut _____ eyes and tried to think how best

_____ could help Plop. _____ decided that Plop was scared

because _____ did not understand what the dark was like.

Surf the Imagination

1 Draw a picture of a dark night.
2 Write how you would see if
you were driving at night;
your bedroom was dark;
you were looking for something in a dark cupboard;
you were walking along the street in the dark.

Mouse Search

1 There are many types of owl.
Find out about as many as
you can.
2 Make a scrapbook of some
bird photographs.
3 Find out about creatures that
can see in the dark.

Look out below!

The Misty Family, Mum, Dad, Odle and Mo, are on holiday from outer space in their Zome Kraft. They are on their way to visit a strange planet called Earth where creatures they call Two-Leggers live. Find out what happens when Odle manages to launch his sister towards earth before the Zome Kraft lands.

The Zome Kraft hissed through Outer Space and entered the solar system, left of the sun and right of the moon, where it altered course and began to slow down, spinning towards its destination.

'Commence Earth Approach!' ordered Mum Misty, crouching over the Control Panel.

'Commence Approach!' echoed Dad.

'Is that it?' asked Odle.

'What?'

'Earth,' said Odle, and he bam-bam-bammed what he could see of it on the see-screen with his space gun.

'That's Earth,' said Dad. 'Stay away from those launch buttons, Odle!'

'I'm hungry!' little Mo announced.

'You're always hungry,' said Odle.

'But I *am*,' said Mo. 'Isn't there anything to eat?'

'Zero 3900, descending,' said Mum. 'Give her a food block, somebody.'

Dad gave Mo a food block. It was small, about the size of a chocolate bar, but it was packed with energy.

'Yummy!' said Mo, taking a big bite.

'I bet you'll be sick,' said Odle.

'*You* make me sick!' said Mo.

'Not as sick as you'll be if an old Two-Legger Earth Monster gets you,' said Odle.

'Odle!' snapped Mum and Dad Misty, together.

'Are there many Earth Monsters, Mum?' Mo asked, nervously.

'Lots!' said Odle. 'There are Flappers that fly and Finners that swim and Roarers that roar in the jungle and horrible Two-Leggers and ...'

'They're all very small, Mo dear,' said Mum, quickly. 'You *know* that.'

'Will they eat me?' asked Mo, finishing the last bite of her food block.

'No,' said Mum.

'Yes!' said Odle.

'ODLE!' said Dad.

'And spit out the pips,' Odle added, cheerfully.

'Any more of that and I'll turn this Kraft round and go straight home, Odle,' said Mum Misty, firmly. 'No holiday. No going about to look at Earth Monsters. NOTHING! Understand?'

'Yes, Mum,' said Odle, and he went back to bam-bam-bamming Earth.

'I want to go home,' said Mo, climbing into her Pod, where she snuggled down in comfort.

'Zero 3500, descending,' said Mum.

'Zero 3500, descending,' confirmed Dad.

'Mo likes being at home,' said Odle. 'She doesn't enjoy Going Spaces.'

'Going Spaces is good for you,' said Mum. 'It broadens the mind.'

'What mind?' said Odle. 'She hasn't got one!'
He bounced over to Mo's Pod, and bam-bam-
bammed what he could see of her.

'Odle!' said both of the big Mistys, angrily.

'Stay away from those launch buttons, Odle!' added
Dad Misty. 'How many more times must I tell you?'

'Sorry,' said Odle.

'Don't say sorry unless you mean it,' said Mum.
'Entering Orbit.'

'Entering Orbit,' Dad repeated.

The Zome Kraft began to spin slowly round the earth.
The lid of Mo's Pod slid back.

'What are *those*, Mum?' Mo asked, pointing at the big
shapes on the see-screen. 'Are they Monsters?'

'Those are Mountains, Mo. I've told you before.
The Earth Monsters are small, even the Two-Leggers.
They are titchy little things compared to us.'

'They eat other Earth Monsters,
Two-Leggers do,' said Odle.

'I don't want to go to
Earth,' said Mo. 'I wish
we'd stayed at home.'

'You'll have a Two-Legger disguise on, Mo,' said Mum. 'You'll be able to walk around Earth and the Two-Leggers won't know you're not one of them.'

'I don't want to look like them,' said Mo. 'They're stupid, and ugly.'

'Don't be silly, Mo,' said Mum.

'Those are houses, just below us,' said Dad, hurriedly changing the subject.

'What are *houses*, Dad?' asked Odle, peering at them.

'Two-Legger Dwellings, Odle,' said Dad. 'The things they live in.'

'Why do they live packed close together, like that?' asked Odle, peering at the see-screen. 'All squashed up tight against each other?'

'They don't know any better,' said Mum.

'They're not very bright,' said Dad.

'I want to go home,' said Mo, in a sulky voice. She climbed inside her Pod again, and slid the door closed over her head.

'Bam!' shouted Odle, dancing around Mo's Pod, and making faces at her. 'Bam-bam-bam-bam! Scared of old Two-Leggers! Scaredy Mo! Bam-bam-bam-b-a-a-a-m!'

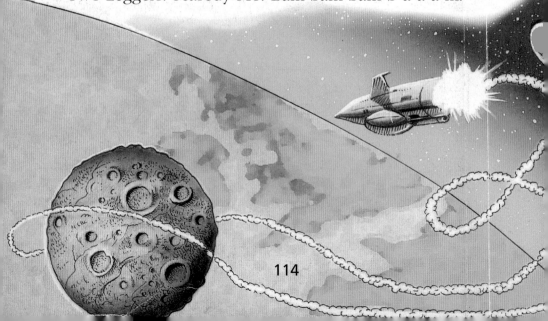

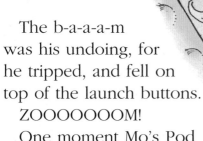

The b-a-a-a-m
was his undoing, for
he tripped, and fell on
top of the launch buttons.

ZOOOOOOOM!

One moment Mo's Pod
was there, with Mo in it,
and the next it wasn't.

'Mo!' Mum screamed.

Mo was gone, powering ahead
of the Zome Kraft with her Pod Boosters ablaze.
There was nothing Mum and Dad could do to stop her
descent to Earth, and nothing poor Mo could do either,
because she was too small to know how her Pod
worked.

Down, down, down the Pod sped, down down
down to ...

The Blue Misty Monsters by Catherine Sefton,
Faber & Faber

Blarney Blasts

 1 You see the Misty's Zome Kraft approaching Earth. You phone Gardaí to tell them about what you have seen. Your partner answers the call. What is said?

2 The day after Mo lands on Earth you find her and bring her to your house. What do you tell her about life on Earth?

Log Jogging

Look at your Log Jogging list on page 192.

Pick one suggestion and write about it.

Tale and Detail

1 What was the number of the Zome Kraft?
2 Who was travelling in the Zome Kraft?
3 What did Odle mean by Two-Leggers, Flappers, Finners, Roarers?
4 Why were the Misty Family travelling to Earth?

Undercover Work

1 Were the Blue Misty Monsters bigger or smaller than humans? How do you know?
2 How did Dad describe houses?
3 How was Mo's pod launched?
4 Why could nobody help Mo?
5 In what ways did Odle try to frighten his sister?

116

Word Wizardry

A writer makes a story more interesting by using different kinds of words. In this story the writer uses many words instead of said. Can you find six other ways of writing said in this story?

Surf the Imagination

1 Draw your own space-ship. Show the outside and the inside.
2 Make a model of your space-ship at home.
3 Draw your own family of aliens. Give them names and talk about them.
4 Imagine that Mo comes to stay at your house while she waits for her family to find her. How does she help you?

Mouse Search

1 Find out the names of the planets in our solar system.
2 Earth has one natural satellite called the Moon. Find one other planet in our solar system that has a moon.
3 Which planet in our solar system has rings around it?

Cold chips

Mo has landed in a back garden on Earth and is very frightened. The rest of the Misty family land and begin to look for her. They try to disguise themselves to look like Two-Leggers, but do not know that people are not usually blue! Watch out for what happens to Darren, Ralph and Bruno's dad when the Misty family meet him. Read about what happens to Mo when she meets some of Earth's four-legged creatures.

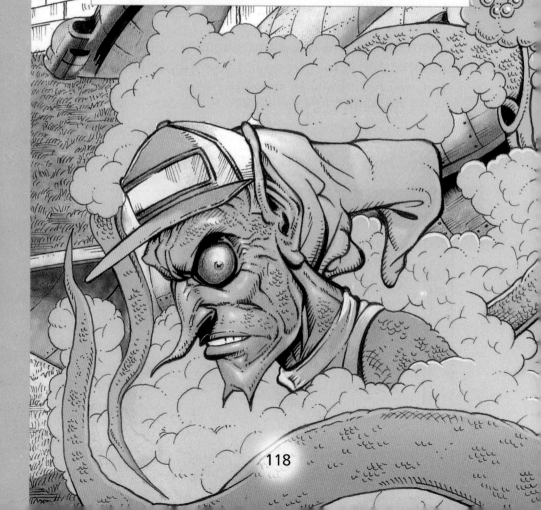

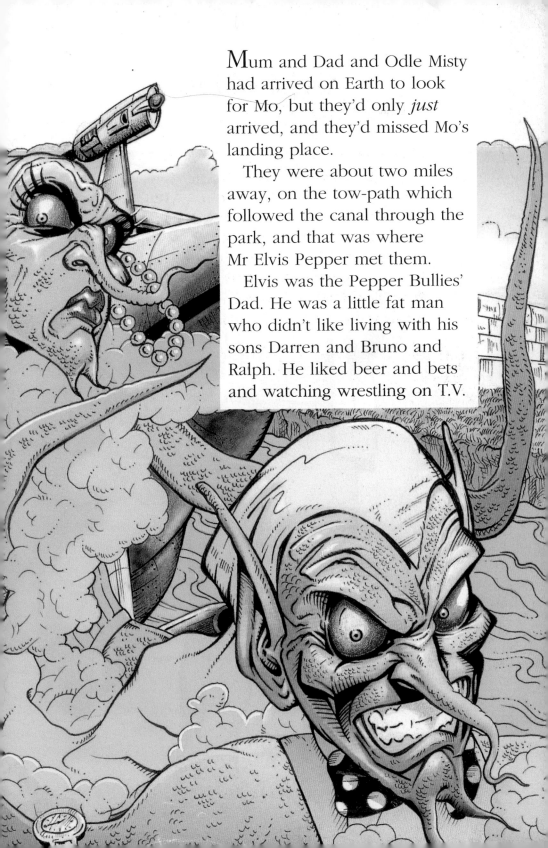

Mum and Dad and Odle Misty had arrived on Earth to look for Mo, but they'd only *just* arrived, and they'd missed Mo's landing place.

They were about two miles away, on the tow-path which followed the canal through the park, and that was where Mr Elvis Pepper met them.

Elvis was the Pepper Bullies' Dad. He was a little fat man who didn't like living with his sons Darren and Bruno and Ralph. He liked beer and bets and watching wrestling on T.V.

As a result he spent most of his time in the pub, where Darren and Bruno and Ralph couldn't go.

He was on his way home from the pub with a parcel of fish and chips when he noticed the mist. He stopped chip-nibbling, and looked. There was something odd about the mist. It had a blue crinkly edge.

It touched Elvis's fat little legs.

There was a crackle, and a flash, and Elvis was *fixed*, with a half-nibbled chip held up in front of his nose.

Two huge misty shapes loomed out of the darkness, followed by another one, about half the size.

'Do you think it might be dangerous, dear?' asked the first shape, wisping round Elvis.

It didn't *speak*. There was no sound, but Elvis knew what it was saying. He could hear the words clearly in his mind, although his ears had nothing to do with it.

'It's all right,' said the second shape. 'I've *fixed* it.'

'It's a Two-Legger!' said the half-sized shape. 'Bam-bam-bam!'

'Stop it, Odle!' said the first shape. 'Stop it at once.'

'I've stopped,' said the half-sized shape.
'I've exterminated the rotten Two-Legger!'

'That's enough, Odle,' said the second shape firmly.
'You must learn to be polite to creatures on strange
planets. You mustn't hurt their feelings.'

'Have they got *feelings*?' asked the half-sized shape.

'Of course, dear,' said the first shape. 'All living things
have feelings. Two-Leggers are not very well developed
creatures, but you must be polite and kind to them,
just the same.'

'Why?' asked the half-sized shape.

'How would you like it if *they*
were rude to *you*?' said the first
shape. 'They might think *you*
look rotten.'

'But I don't,' said the
half-sized shape. It drifted
carefully round Elvis.

'What's that?' it said, closing in
on the fish and chips.

'I dread to think,' said the first shape,
with a shudder.

'That's its food,' said the second shape.

122

'Why does it carry its food round in parcels?' asked the half-sized shape. 'Why doesn't it eat food blocks, like us?'

'I expect the Two-Leggers haven't invented food blocks yet, Odle,' said the first shape. 'Don't go too close, dear. You never know with strangers. It might be hostile.'

'It's awfully ugly,' said the half-sized shape.

'I don't suppose the Two-Legger knows it is ugly, dear,' said the first shape. 'It moves about on *those*, and it grabs with those.'

Elvis decided that they were discussing his arms and legs. He thought he was going mad. What was happening to him *couldn't* be happening.

'I want to unfix it,' said the half-sized shape. 'I want to see it moving on those and grabbing things with those.'

'It's time we started hunting for Mo,' said the first shape. 'We've no time to play games! Why doesn't she put the bleep on?'

'Because she's stupid!' said the half-sized shape.

'That's quite enough from you, Odle!' said the second shape. 'If it wasn't for you, we wouldn't be in this mess.'

'Wait until I get you home, Odle!' said the first shape. 'Launching your poor little sister off on to Earth like that ...'

The three shapes drifted away from Elvis, leaving him

fixed in position, with his fish and chip supper growing colder and colder.

He didn't wake up until past nine o'clock, when the park gates had closed, and by then he couldn't remember quite what had happened to him.

The garden behind Number 73 Edgeworth Street was quiet, except for the creaking of Spud's rusty swing. Spud and his parents had gone to bed.

Nobody was awake, except Mo.

She hovered at the end of the garden, a pale blue blob of light in the crook of the apple tree. She was hungry, she was cold, and she was alone on a strange planet.

'*Please* come, Mum!' Mo whispered.

Mum didn't come.

Instead, something horrible happened.

An Earth Monster came into the garden.

It was a very small Earth Monster. It had four things to stand on, and a swishy thing at the back and shiny green lights at the front. It looked like a Roarer, but it was much too small, and anyway it wasn't in the jungle. It came padding towards Mo. It had black and white hair all over it, and a soft pink button between the green lights. It settled down close to Mo.

'I wish it would go away,' Mo thought, but it didn't go. It was waiting for something. It twitched the swishy thing, softly.

125

Something else was moving in the darkness.

Another Monster! Mo didn't know what it was either, but it was *very very* small, much smaller than the one who was too small to be a roarer.

The tiny Monster was creeping along, and Mo knew that the Monster with the shiny green lights was watching it.

The Monster with the shiny green lights *pounced*.

There was a terrible squeal. Mo couldn't bear to look.

When she did, the Earth Monster with the shiny green lights was padding away from her. It held the tiny Monster, struggling, in its mouth.

Earth Monsters ate each other! She had seen it happen.

If small black and white ones with green lights and pink buttons did that, what would big ones like the Two-Leggers do, if they got the chance?

Mo had had enough. Bleep or no bleep, she was going back into her Pod. The Pod couldn't bleep if it was full size, but that didn't matter. It was warm and cosy and safe.

That was when Mo discovered that her Pod wasn't where she thought it was, and it wasn't bleeping either.

'Oh *Mummy*!'

Mo searched frantically, but she couldn't find the Pod, even though she divided the space up into squares, and searched each square in turn.

Mo swirled miserably round the garden.

'How can they find me without the bleep? They won't be able to! I'll be trapped here for ever and ever and ever!'

It was a long time before Mo went to sleep, and when she did it was an unhappy sleep. Her mind was filled with nightmares about Two-Leggers and Jungle-Roarers

and huge Earth Monsters with green lights and pink
noses. She felt very small, and very weak, because she
hadn't eaten for ages. Her energy was draining away
and, as it went, some of the blue-ness drained out of her
as well. She grew paler and paler and paler.

Mo was too small for a Big Adventure, all by herself
on a Strange Planet.

The Blue Misty Monsters by Catherine Sefton, Faber & Faber

Blarney Blasts

1 Act out the conversation that occurs the next time Elvis meets his friends when he tells them about meeting the strange creatures.

2 The cat in the story sees Mo and in its surprise, drops the mouse.
The three creatures have a conversation. What do the cat and the mouse tell Mo about life on Earth?

Log Jogging

Look at your Log Jogging list on page 192.

Pick one suggestion and write about it.

Tale and Detail

1 What was in Elvis Pepper's parcel?
2 At what time did Elvis wake up?
3 Whose fault was it that Mo was missing?
4 Where did Mo land?
5 How did Mo search for her pod?

Undercover Work

1 How did Elvis know what the Blue Misty Monsters were saying?
2 What did Dad Misty mean when he said 'I've fixed it'?
3 What opinion did Odle have of Elvis's appearance?
4 What did Elvis think of the strange shapes?
5 What were the shiny green lights on the Earth monster?
6 What happened between the two small creatures in the garden?

Word Wizardry

When you write about doing things in
the past, the **doing** word changes.
For example 'I **play** today' becomes
'I **played** yesterday'. Change the words in the
sentences below to become **past** words.

> I come to school yesterday. I run for the bus and
> get on it. At school I take off my coat and sit down.
> We listen during the day and go outside and run,
> play and jump up and fall down at lunch time.

Surf the Imagination

1 Imagine that you travel to another
   planet. Describe how you get there
   and what happens. Draw a picture of
   the planet and what you find there.
2 How would an alien describe:
   a dog? a car? a horse? a child? a flower?
3 Read the poem, The Alien, on page 4 of the Poetry Book.

Mouse Search

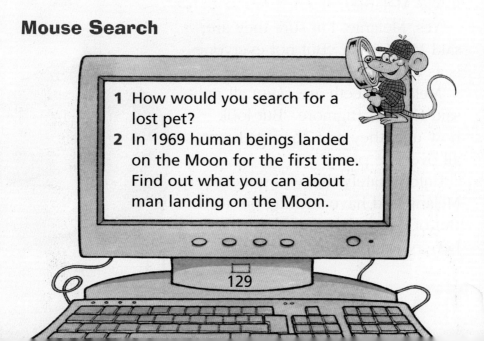

1 How would you search for a
   lost pet?
2 In 1969 human beings landed
   on the Moon for the first time.
   Find out what you can about
   man landing on the Moon.

129

Dental problems

When the new teacher, Mr Majeika, arrives at St Barty's School on a magic carpet, Class Three realise that he is no ordinary teacher. Something has to be done about Hamish Bigmore, the class nuisance, and sometimes it takes a little magic. How will Hamish behave when the school visitor arrives?

'Mr Potter wants everyone to clean their teeth very thoroughly tomorrow,' said Mr Majeika to Class Three, one afternoon about a week before the end of term. 'There's a dentist coming to teach you about careful brushing, and how to fight tooth decay, and Mr Potter says he doesn't want everyone's mouths looking and smelling like the insides of old dustbins.'

'Please, Mr Magic, my teeth are *always* clean,' said a voice. It was Melanie.

'Yes, Melanie, I'm sure they are,' said Mr Majeika. 'But not everyone is as careful as you.'

'Melanie's teeth are *clean* all right,' said Hamish Bigmore. 'But look how ugly they are! They stick out all over the place.'

Unfortunately this was quite true. Melanie did have sticking-out teeth. But of course being told this made her cry even louder than usual.

130

'Boo-hoo! I hate you, Hamish Bigmore, you're *horrid*!' she wailed.

'Don't you call *me* horrid,' answered Hamish. 'Just think how horrid *you* look, with those teeth. In fact you look just like Count Dracula! Melanie's got teeth like a vampire! Ya, horrid old vampire!'

'Be quiet, Hamish Bigmore,' said Mr Majeika. But Hamish, as usual, wouldn't pay any attention. 'Vampire! Vampire!' he shouted. 'Melanie looks like a vampire!'

Mr Majeika suddenly lost his temper. 'I'll show you who's a vampire!' he cried, and pointed a finger at Hamish.

Hamish Bigmore opened his mouth to say something rude — and then stopped, because everyone was suddenly laughing at him. 'Vampire! Vampire!' they were shouting.

132

'What's got into you, you sillies?' he asked them. But they would only answer: 'Vampire! Vampire!'

'Here,' said Pandora Green, 'take a look at this'. She kept a pocket-mirror in her desk for putting on lipstick, when Mr Majeika wasn't looking. Now she held it up to Hamish Bigmore.

He stared in the mirror, then turned on Mr Majeika. 'Look what you've done, Mr Magic!' he shouted.

It was perfectly true. Hamish Bigmore had suddenly grown vampire's teeth.

They were very long and pointed, and stuck right out of his mouth. Two were especially long and sharp. It was as nasty a sight as anything in the horror films on television.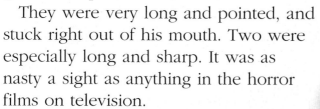

'Oh dear, oh dear,' Mr Majeika was saying. 'I seem to have done it again. These old spells just come back into my head when I least expect them, and then I say them to myself without thinking, and then hey presto! the damage is done.'

'But surely you know how to take *this* spell off him?' asked Jody. 'It can't be as difficult as the frog.'

Mr Majeika shook his head. 'It's quite an easy one,' he said. 'In fact you don't need a spell to get rid of the vampire teeth,

133

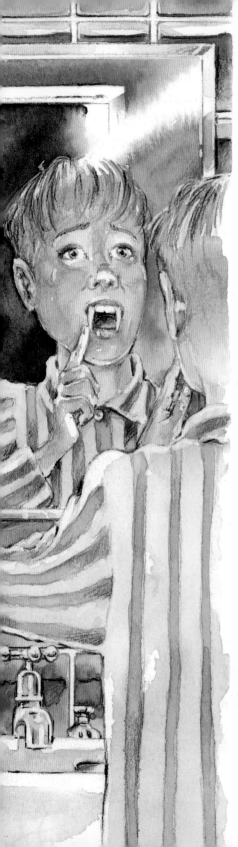

I remember that. Hamish himself
has to *do* something to have his
teeth become normal again.
But I can't for the life of me think
what it is.'

Hamish Bigmore himself had
been sitting silently through this.
Now he snarled between his
vampire teeth: 'Well, if you can't
take these teeth away, I'm going
to *use* them. I'll be a real vampire
and bite you all! And you know
what happens when you're bitten
by a vampire? You become a
vampire yourself! Ha! ha!'

'Don't be silly,' said Mr Majeika.
'You're not a real vampire.
You just happen to have grown
a set of vampire's teeth. But I can
tell you that if you start behaving
in a foolish fashion, Hamish
Bigmore, you can be sure of one
thing — those teeth will never go
away. Just you put a scarf around
your face to hide them, and go
home quietly, and tell everyone
there that you've got toothache,
and go straight to bed, and with
luck in the morning they'll
have gone.'

For once, Hamish Bigmore did
as he was told.

But the next morning the

134

vampire teeth were still there. Thomas and Pete could see them the moment Hamish Bigmore came into Class Three and unwrapped the scarf from around his face. 'Whatever did your mum and dad say?' asked Pete.

'They're away,' said Hamish. 'There's an old aunt of mine looking after me, and she's too short-sighted to notice. Mr Magic should go to prison for doing this to me!'

'It was all your own fault,' said Thomas. 'But what is the dentist going to say?'

This was exactly the thought that crossed Mr Majeika's mind when he arrived in the classroom and saw that Hamish's teeth hadn't changed back in the night. 'Oh dear,' he said, 'this is going to be very awkward'.

When the dentist came, it proved to be a lady. Hamish Bigmore had been put in a far corner of the room, in the hope that she would not look at him, but she went carefully round everyone in the class, making them all open their mouths.

'Now,' she said brightly, peering into Thomas's, 'have you been brushing away regularly with Betty Brush and Tommy Toothpaste? You must remember to fight Dan Decay, and Percy Plaque, or horrid old Terry Toothache will come along and make your life a misery.'

'She's treating us as if we were

toddlers in the nursery class,' grumbled Jody. But there was nothing anyone could do to stop the lady dentist chattering away in this daft fashion. Finally she got to Hamish Bigmore, who, on Mr Majeika's instructions, had the scarf wrapped tightly around his mouth.

'Who have we here?' she said brightly. Hamish got to his feet and started to make for the door.

'He's not feeling very well,' said Mr Majeika. 'I think he needs to go to the lavatory.'

'Well, he can just wait a minute,' said the lady dentist firmly. 'Let's unwrap that scarf, my little friend, and see what we find beneath. Are Dan Decay and Percy Plaque lurking there, or have you been a good boy and used Betty Brush and Tommy Toothpaste?'

Hamish Bigmore had had enough of this. He pulled the scarf from his face and bared his horrid long pointed teeth at the lady dentist.

'No,' he cried. 'I haven't been a good boy! I'm Victor the Vampire and I'm going to drink your blood!'

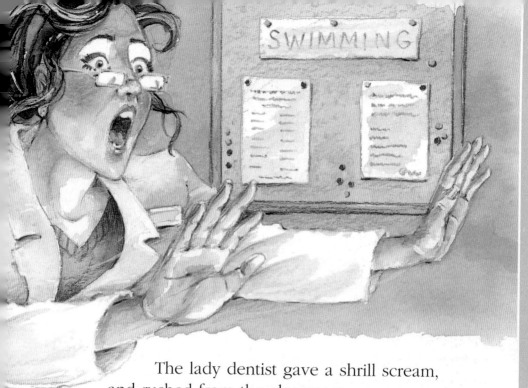

The lady dentist gave a shrill scream, and rushed from the classroom.

'Now really,' said Mr Majeika to Hamish Bigmore when order had been restored, 'that was *not* necessary. You might have given her a heart attack.' As it was, the lady dentist had driven away very fast in her little car, saying she never wanted to look at schoolchildren's teeth again.

'I'm sorry you've still got those teeth,' continued Mr Majeika to Hamish, 'but really, behaving so naughtily won't help. I'm still trying to find out what it is you must do to get rid of them — I've been looking through all my old spell-books — and in the meantime I advise you to be as good as possible ...' Suddenly he stopped.

'What's the matter?' asked Jody.

'I've just remembered!' cried Mr Majeika in delight. 'I've remembered what Hamish has to do to get rid of those teeth! *He has to be good*!'

Mr Majeika by Humphrey Carpenter, Puffin Books

Blarney Blasts

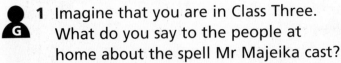

G **1** Imagine that you are in Class Three. What do you say to the people at home about the spell Mr Majeika cast?

P **2** Tell a partner what happens when you visit the dentist?

P **3** Talk about other stories you have heard or read where spells were cast. What happened?

Log Jogging

Look at your Log Jogging list on page 192.

Pick one suggestion and write about it.

Tale and Detail

1 Why did Mr Majeika want the children to clean their teeth?

2 What happened to Hamish's teeth?

3 Who gave Hamish the mirror?

4 What things did the dentist give people's names to?

5 How could the spell be reversed?

Undercover Work

1 What did the dentist want to teach the children?

2 What hurt Melanie's feelings?

3 Why did Hamish's parents not say anything about his teeth?

4 Explain how the spell was cast on Hamish.

5 What frightened the dentist?

6 In what ways was Hamish Bigmore a very disagreeable boy?

138

Word Wizardry

Choose a word from the box that could be used instead of the green words in the sentences below. Tick each word as you use it.

silly	giggling	weep
jail	quietly	See

Suddenly everyone was **laughing** at him.
'**Look** what you've done, Mr Magic!'
Hamish Bigmore himself had been sitting **silently** through this.
If you start behaving in a **foolish** fashion, those teeth will never go away.
Mr Majeika should go to **prison** for doing this!
Being told this made her **cry** louder than usual.

Surf the Imagination

1 Imagine that you are Melanie. How do you feel when you see that Hamish Bigmore has vampire's teeth?
2 Make up your own names for your toothbrush, shoes, schoolbag.
3 Make up a spell you would like to cast on someone to teach them a lesson.
4 Draw a picture of your teeth.

Mouse Search

1 Find out how to look after your teeth.
2 Find out the names of your teeth. What job does each of our teeth do?

Josie Smith and the birthday flowers

On Saturday morning it rained and rained and in the afternoon it stopped.

Josie Smith stood on one leg and pulled her sock up. Then she stood on the other leg and pulled her other sock up. Then she put her wellingtons on and her blue jacket.

'Put a hat on!' shouted Josie Smith's mum from the kitchen, 'and tie your scarf properly!'

Josie Smith pulled a horrible face. She put on a woolly hat that itched and a woolly scarf that itched even more, winding it round and round so that she wouldn't get tonsillitis.

Every time she went out her mum said,
'If you don't tie that scarf properly, you'll
end up with tonsillitis'.

Josie Smith went out and shut the door
behind her. Josie's house was number 1. It was
the same as all the other houses in the street and
the street was the same as all the other streets on
the side of the hill and on the top of the hill there
was a tower. At the bottom of the hill was
Josie Smith's school and the main road and the shops
and the mills with tall chimneys.

141

Josie Smith saw Eileen next door sitting on the step nursing a doll wrapped in a shawl.

'Are you playing?' Eileen said.

'No, I'm not,' said Josie Smith. 'I'm busy.'

'No, you're not,' said Eileen.

'Yes I am,' said Josie Smith. 'It's my mum's birthday and I'm going to get her a present and a birthday card.'

'I bet you've got no money,' Eileen said.

'Yes I have,' said Josie Smith.

'You haven't.'

'I have. I've got 50p,' said Josie Smith.

'You're a liar,' Eileen said, rocking her doll backwards and forwards. 'My mum says I haven't to play with you because you tell lies.'

'I don't want to play with you, anyway,' Josie Smith said. 'You and your stupid doll.' And she went off down the street, making as much noise as she could with her wellingtons. When she passed Gary Grimes's house he came to the door. He had a grey cardigan on with a zip up the front and grey slippers with zips up the front as well.

'I can't play out,' Gary Grimes said. 'I've got bronchitis, but we can play in if you want.'

'I'm not playing,' Josie Smith said. 'It's my mum's birthday and I'm going to get her a present and a birthday card.'

She waited to see if Gary Grimes would say she hadn't got any money like Eileen, but Gary Grimes went in and shut the door.

Josie Smith went on down the street making a noise
with her wellingtons. The pavements were wet and in
the big puddles she could see dirty clouds going past the
upside down chimneys but it didn't start raining. At the
end of the street was the spare ground where there was
grass and cinders and the things that people threw away.
Josie Smith searched all over the grass and all over the
cinders looking for bottles to take back to the shop.
It wasn't really a lie when she told Eileen she had 50p
because she was going to get it soon. Josie Smith found
two small bottles in the grass and a big bottle that was
nearly buried in the cinders. She had to dig for it with a
stick. She held the bottles tight against her chest and
carried them to Mrs Chadwick's shop.

'I've brought these back,' she said, and put them up on
the counter.

Mrs Chadwick looked mad.

'Josie Smith!' she shouted.

'Look at all the dirt you've put on my counter!'

Josie Smith reached up and tried to rub the dirt away with her sleeve but Mrs Chadwick still looked mad. She was holding the big bottle between two fingers and pulling a funny face.

'Those other two want throwing away,' Mrs Chadwick said. 'They're non-returnable. But I suppose I can give you something on this. What do you want today? Toffees or Spanish?'

'I don't want toffees today,' Josie Smith said. 'It's my mum's birthday and I'm going to get her a present and a birthday card.'

'Here then,' said Mrs Chadwick. 'You can give her this.' And she held out a bun with white icing on it and a cherry on top.

'I don't want that,' said Josie Smith.

'My mum buys cakes on Saturdays. I'm buying her some flowers because she hasn't got any.'

145

Mrs Chadwick got some money
from the till and put it on the
counter. Josie Smith reached up
for it.

'Thank you, Mrs Chadwick!'
she shouted, and ran out of the shop.

'Wait a minute!' shouted Mrs Chadwick behind her,
but Josie Smith couldn't wait and she ran away. She ran
and ran until there were no more houses and she came to
Mr Scowcroft's allotment. Mr Scowcroft had cabbages in
his allotment and a shed with hens. Mr Scowcroft was

146

standing amongst the cabbages with his pipe in his mouth, looking at the sky.

'It'll come on to rain again in a while,' Mr Scowcroft said.

'How do you know?' asked Josie Smith. But Mr Scowcroft didn't say anything. He just made a whistling noise with his pipe.

'Do you want me to dig a bit for you, Mr Scowcroft?' asked Josie Smith.

'Girls can't dig,' Mr Scowcroft said, still looking at the sky, 'not so well as boys can'.

'I can dig,' said Josie Smith.

'And then there's the worms,' Mr Scowcroft said. 'You have to collect the worms you find to give to the hens. Girls don't like worms.'

'I like worms, Mr Scowcroft,' Josie Smith said, shutting her eyes as she said it, because it was a lie.

'Well,' said Mr Scowcroft, 'we'll see how you do'. And he gave her a big spade and a tin for the worms.

Josie Smith began to dig. She put her wellington on the edge of the spade like she'd seen Mr Scowcroft do but the spade didn't go in. She stood on the spade with both wellingtons and then it went in. Josie Smith dug and dug and when she saw a worm, she bent down and

put it in the tin, keeping her eyes almost closed so she wouldn't see how much it wriggled. At first, when she started digging, she felt cold, but then she felt hotter and hotter. She took off the itchy scarf and hung it on the fence.

'Why don't the hens get their own worms, Mr Scowcroft?' she asked.

'They'd peck at my cabbages,' Mr Scowcroft said, 'if I let them out'.

Josie Smith dug and dug until she couldn't dig any more.

'I have to go now, Mr Scowcroft,' she said.

'Aye,' said Mr Scowcroft, and he went inside his hen shed.

Josie Smith waited. Was he not going to give her any wages? He always gave the boys wages when they dug.

'Mr Scowcroft!' shouted Josie Smith. 'It's my mum's birthday and I have to get her a present and a birthday card.'

Mr Scowcroft came out. 'Birthday is it?' he said. 'She'll have a nice birthday surprise when she sees how black you've got yourself. Here,' Mr Scowcroft held out his hand. There were two eggs on it. 'You can give these to your mum,' he said. 'Two brown eggs with red specks. New laid. That's a nice present.'

'I don't want them,' Josie Smith said. 'My mum buys eggs on Saturdays. I'm buying her some flowers because she hasn't got any.'

Mr Scowcroft sucked on his pipe and made a whistling noise but he didn't say anything. Then he pulled some coins out of this trousers and held them out.

'Thank you, Mr Scowcroft!' shouted Josie Smith, and she started running.

'Hoy!' shouted Mr Scowcroft. 'Hoy! Wait a minute!'

But Josie Smith was frightened that he might change his mind about the wages and she ran away as fast as she could.

When she was out of breath, she stopped and sat down on the doorstep of Mr Kefford's greengrocer's shop and emptied the dirt out of her wellingtons and pulled her socks up. Then she counted her money. 30p. It wasn't enough. The door of the greengrocer's shop opened behind her.

'What do you think you're doing?' said Mr Kefford, 'sunbathing?'

'No,' said Josie Smith. 'It's cold.'

'Cold?' said Mr Kefford. 'Rubbish! Sun's cracking the pavement. Up you get now. I have to sweep out.'

'D'you want me to sweep out for you?' asked Josie Smith.

'If you know how to do it properly.'

'I'm a good sweeper,' Josie Smith said. 'I sweep hard.'

'Right, then,' said Mr Kefford. 'Let's see what you can do.'

Josie Smith started to sweep. She swept up cabbage leaves and a sprout and a bit of parsley and a lot of brown dust from the potatoes and she shovelled it all into the bag that Mr Kefford gave her.

'Well,' said Mr Kefford, 'you're no bigger than a fourpenny rabbit but you're a good little sweeper and no mistake. I'd better give you some wages.' And he looked round his shop.

'It's my mum's birthday,' Josie Smith said. 'And I want to get her a present and a birthday card.'

She waited, looking up at Mr Kefford who was very tall and had big red hands with black cracks in them.

'Well, now, let's see …,' said Mr Kefford,
and he went to get something from a crate. 'Here you
are,' he said. 'You can take this home for your mum.'
And he held out a big red shiny apple.

'I don't want that,' said Josie Smith. 'My mum buys
apples every Saturday. I want to get her some flowers
because she hasn't got any.'

'I see,' said Mr Kefford. 'I see. That's how it is, is it.'
Mr Kefford's big red hand went inside the pocket of his
green overall and pulled out some coins. Josie Smith
took the money and ran out of the shop shouting,
'Thank you, Mr Kefford!'

'Hoy!' shouted Mr Kefford. 'Hoy, wait a minute!'

But Josie Smith was running down the road as fast as
she could. When she was out of breath, she stopped and

counted her money. 50p! She started running
again and ran until she got to the flower shop. It was
going dark and the light was on in the flower shop
window. Josie Smith stood with her nose pressed to the
glass, choosing. While she was choosing, she stamped
her feet in her wellingtons because they were freezing
cold. There were all sorts of flowers in the window,
pink ones, yellow ones, blue ones and even some with
stripes. But the best flowers were the ones right in the
middle. Great big red roses in a white vase. Josie Smith
opened the door and went in.

Josie Smith by Magdalen Nabb, Collins

153

Blarney Blasts

1 Mrs Chadwick, Mr Scowcroft and Mr Kefford meet each other and talk about Josie Smith. Act out the conversation with two partners.

2 Act out with a partner the conversation that happened in the flowershop between Josie and the shopkeeper.

Log Jogging

Look at your Log Jogging list on page 192.

Pick one suggestion and write about it.

Tale and Detail

1 On which day of the week did this story happen?
2 Why was Josie too busy to play?
3 Name all the people Josie spoke to in the story.
4 Name all the things Josie did to earn money.
5 Describe Mr Kefford.
6 What colours are named in the story?

Undercover Work

1 Why did Josie search the spare ground?
2 What happened each time Josie got her money?
3 How did Josie show Mr Scowcroft that he was wrong about girls?
4 How many jobs did Josie do to earn the money she wanted? Name them.
5 Why did the grown-ups in the story offer sweets, fruit and eggs for the work Josie did?

154

Word Wizardry

Put a circle around the silent letters of the words in the box below:

ghost	lamb	knot
comb	ghetto	bomb
knob	limb	knife
knew		

Surf the Imagination

1 Design and draw a rainy-day outfit.
2 Imagine that you have to work to earn money to buy a present for someone. Tell about the jobs you would do.
3 Write about your house and its surroundings.

Mouse Search

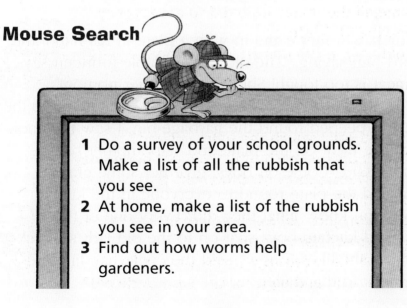

1 Do a survey of your school grounds. Make a list of all the rubbish that you see.
2 At home, make a list of the rubbish you see in your area.
3 Find out how worms help gardeners.

155

In the kitchen

The narrator of the story is on holidays with his grandmother in the *Hotel Magnificent* in Bournemouth. Pretending to be members of the Royal Society for the Prevention of Cruelty to Children (RSPCC), the most gruesome gang of witches has gathered to hear the Grand High Witch reveal her plan for the extinction of all children in England. When the witches realise that the boy, who has been hiding, has overheard their wicked plan, they change him into a mouse. He manages to return to his grandmother and tell her what has happened. Together, they decide on a plan to save other children, by giving the witches a taste of their own medicine — in other words, an overdose of their very own *Delayed Action Mouse-Maker!* But a hotel kitchen is an extremely dangerous place for a mouse to be seen.

Just then, a waiter came in with a plate in his hand and I heard him saying, 'The old hag on table fourteen says this meat is too tough! She wants another portion!'
One of the cooks said, 'Gimme her plate!' I dropped to the floor and peeped round the garbage-bin. I saw the cook scrape the meat off the plate and slap another bit on. Then he said, 'Come on boys, give her some gravy!'
He carried the plate round to everyone in the kitchen and do you know what they did? Every one of those cooks and kitchen-boys spat on to the old lady's plate! 'See how she likes it now!' said the cook, handing the plate back to the waiter.

Quite soon another waiter came in and he shouted, 'Everyone in the big RSPCC party wants the soup!' That's when I started sitting up and taking notice. I was all ears now. I edged a bit farther round the garbage-bin so that I could see everything that was going on in the kitchen. A man with a tall white hat who must have been the head chef shouted, 'Put the soup for the big party in the larger silver soup-tureen!'

I saw the head chef place a huge silver basin on to the wooden side-bench that ran along the whole length of the kitchen against the opposite wall. *Into that silver basin is where the soup is going,* I told myself. *So that's where the stuff in my little bottle must go as well.*

I noticed that high up near the ceiling, above the side-bench, there was a long shelf crammed with saucepans and frying-pans. *If I can somehow clamber up on to that shelf,* I thought, *then*

158

I've got it made. I shall be directly above the silver basin.

But first I must somehow get across to the other side of the kitchen and then up on to the middle shelf. A great idea came to me! Once again, I jumped up and hooked my tail around the handle of the garbage-bin. Then, hanging upside down, I began to swing. Higher and higher I swung. I was remembering the trapeze artist in the circus I had seen last Easter and the way he had got the trapeze swinging higher and higher and higher and had then let go and gone flying through the air. So just at the right moment, at the top of my swing, I let go with my tail and went soaring clear across the kitchen and made a perfect landing on the middle shelf!

By golly, I thought, what marvellous things a mouse can do! And I'm only a beginner!

No one had seen me. They were all far too busy with their pots and pans. From the middle shelf I somehow managed to shinny up a little water-pipe in the corner, and in no time at all I was up on the very top shelf just under the ceiling, among all the saucepans and the frying-pans. I knew that no one could possibly see me

up there. It was a super position, and I began working my way along the shelf until I was directly above the big empty silver basin they were going to pour the soup into. I put down my bottle. I unscrewed the top and crept to the edge of the shelf and quickly poured what was in it straight into the silver basin below. The next moment, one of the cooks came along with a gigantic saucepan of steaming green soup and poured the whole lot into the silver basin. He put the lid on the basin and shouted, 'Soup for the big party all ready to go out!' Then a waiter arrived and carried the silver basin away.

I had done it! Even if I never

got back alive to my grandmother, the witches were still
going to get the Mouse-Maker! I left the empty bottle
behind a large saucepan and began working my way
back along the top shelf. It was much easier to move
about without the bottle. I began using my tail more and
more. I swung from the handle of one saucepan to the
handle of another all the way along that top shelf, while
far below me cooks and waiters were all bustling about
and kettles were steaming and pans were spluttering and
pots were boiling and I thought to myself, *Oh boy, this is
the life! What fun it is to be a mouse doing an exciting
job like this!* I kept right on swinging. I swung most
marvellously from handle to handle, and I was enjoying
myself so much that I completely forgot I was in full
view of anyone in the kitchen who might happen to
glance upwards. What came next happened so quickly
I had no time to save myself. I heard a man's voice
yelling, 'A mouse! Look at that dirty little mouse!' And
I caught a glimpse below me of a white-coated figure in
a tall white hat and then there was a flash of steel as the
carving-knife whizzed through the air and there was a
shoot of pain in the end of my tail and suddenly I was

161

falling and falling head-first towards the floor.

Even as I fell, I knew just what had happened. I knew that the tip of my tail had been cut off and that I was about to crash on to the floor and everyone in the kitchen would be after me.

'A mouse!' they were shouting. 'A mouse! A mouse! Catch it quick!' I hit the floor and jumped up and ran for my life. All around me there were big black boots going *stamp stamp stamp* and I dodged around them and ran and ran and ran, twisting and turning, and dodging and

162

swerving across the kitchen floor. 'Get it!' they were shouting. 'Kill it! Stamp on it!' The whole floor seemed to be full of black boots stamping away at me and I dodged and swerved and twisted and turned and then in sheer desperation, hardly knowing what I was doing, wanting only a place to hide, I ran up the trouser-leg of one of the cooks and clung to his sock!

'Hey!' the cook shouted. 'Jeepers creepers! He's gone up my trouser! Hold on, boys! I'll get him this time!'

The man's hands began slap-slapping at the trouser-leg and now I really *was* going to get smashed if I didn't move quickly. There was only one way to go and that was up.

I dug my little claws into the hairy skin of the man's leg and scuttled upwards, higher and higher, past the calf and past the knee and on to the thigh.

'Holy smoke!' the man

was yelling. 'It's going all the way up! It's going right up my leg!' I heard shrieks of laughter coming from the other cooks but I can promise you I wasn't laughing myself. I was running for my life. The man's hands were slap-slap-slapping all around me and he was jumping up and down as though he was standing on hot bricks, and I kept climbing and I kept dodging and very soon I reached the very top of the trouser-leg and there was nowhere else to go.

'Help! Help! Help!' the man was screaming. 'It's in my knickers! It's running round in my flaming knickers! Get it out! Someone help me to get it out!'

'Take off your trousers, you silly slob!' someone else shouted. 'Pull down your pants and we'll soon catch him!'

I was in the middle of the man's trousers now, in the place where the two trouser-legs meet and the zip begins. It was dark and awfully hot in there. I knew I had to keep going. I dashed onward and found the top of the other trouser-leg. I went down it like greased lightning and came out at the bottom of it and once again I was on the floor. I heard the stupid cook still shouting, 'It's in my trousers!

Get it out! Will somebody *please* help me to get it out before it bites me!' I caught a flashing glimpse of the entire kitchen staff crowding round him and laughing their heads off and nobody saw the little mouse as it flew across the floor and dived into a sack of potatoes.

I burrowed down in among the dirty potatoes and held my breath.

The cook must have started taking his trousers right off because now they were shouting, 'It's not in there! There's no mice in there, you silly twerp!'

'There was! I swear there was!' the man was shouting back. 'You've never *had* a mouse in your trousers! You don't know what it feels like!'

The fact that a tiny little creature like me had caused such a commotion among a bunch of grown-up men gave me a happy feeling. I couldn't help smiling in spite of the pain in my tail.

I stayed where I was until I was sure they had

forgotten about me. Then I crept out of the potatoes and cautiously poked my tiny head over the edge of the sack. Once again the kitchen was all of a bustle with cooks and waiters rushing about everywhere.

I saw the waiter who had come in earlier with the complaint about tough meat coming in again. 'Hey boys!' he shouted. 'I asked the old hag if the new bit of meat was any better and she said it was perfectly delicious! She said it was really tasty!'

I had to get out of that kitchen and back to my grandmother. There was only one way to do this. I must make a dash clear across the floor and out through the door behind one of the waiters. I stayed quite still, watching for my chance. My tail was hurting terribly. I curled it round so as to have a look at it.

About two inches of it were missing and it was bleeding quite a lot. There was a waiter loading up with a batch of plates full of pink ice-cream. He had a plate in each hand and two more balanced on each arm. He went towards the door. He pushed it open with his shoulder. I leapt out of the sack of potatoes and went across that kitchen floor and into the Dining-Room like a streak of light, and I didn't stop running until I was underneath my grandmother's table.

It was lovely to see my grandmother's feet again in those old-fashioned black shoes with their straps and buttons. I shinnied up one of her legs and landed on her lap. 'Hello, Grandmamma!' I whispered. 'I'm back! I did it! I poured it all into their soup!'

Her hand came down and caressed me. 'Well *done*, my darling!' she whispered back. 'Well done you! They are at this very moment eating that soup!' Suddenly, she withdrew her hand. 'You're bleeding!' she whispered. 'My darling, what's happened to you?'

The Witches by Roald Dahl, Puffin Books

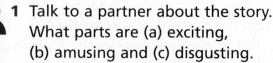

Blarney Blasts

1 Talk to a partner about the story.
What parts are (a) exciting,
(b) amusing and (c) disgusting.

2 You are the cook who made the soup.
Tell what ingredients you have put
into it and tell why you selected them.

Log Jogging

Look at your Log Jogging list on
page 192.

Pick one suggestion and write about it.

Tale and Detail

Make questions for the following answers:

1 They all wanted the soup.
2 The cooks were too busy with
their pots and pans.
3 He managed to shinny up the little
water pipe in the corner.

4 He left the bottle behind a large empty saucepan.
5 The mouse was in his trousers.
6 'Well done my darling.'

Undercover Work

1 How did the narrator of this story work out a way to feed
the Mouse-Maker potion to the witches?

2 Why did a small creature like a mouse
cause such a commotion?

3 How did the narrator know his
grandmother?

168

Word Wizardry

Sometimes the word **and** is used to join up two
sentences. The following sentences, taken from
the story, had been joined by the word **and**.
Write the sentences again to join them, using the word **and**.

I saw the cook scrape the meat off the plate.	He slapped another bit on.
He carried the plate around to everyone in the kitchen.	Do you know what they did?
Quite soon another waiter came in.	He shouted, 'Everyone in the big RSPCC party wants soup'.

Surf the Imagination

1 Write your own recipe for a potion.
What does your potion do?
2 Write a menu for
(a) a dinner that you would like
or
(b) your friend's favourite meal.

Mouse Search

1 Do a survey in your class to find out
(a) everyone's favourite food and
(b) food that people in your class do not like.
In groups, make a bar chart showing the data
you have collected.
2 At home, look at some of the different foods you have.
Find out the ingredients that are used in them
and what countries they come from.
Show this information on a chart.

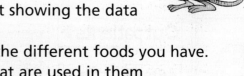

169

I want to go home!

When seven year old Shane Walsh tells his mammy that his leg is too sore to walk on, she sends for the doctor. Shane has to travel miles and miles from the farm where he lives to a children's hospital in Dublin. He doesn't like having doctors and nurses around him, talking about him as if he wasn't there, and wants to go home.

Shane watched the white ceiling pass by above him. He was on a trolley. He winced as the man pushing it jerked it round a corner and the pain in his leg bit into him like a burn.

He wished he could hold Da's hand, but he was seven now. He was a big boy.

Da put his hand over Shane's and gave it a squeeze. 'It's OK, son.' He forgot to take it away again. Shane held on to Da's fingers tightly. His leg wasn't really sore. Not that sore, anyway. Not if he didn't stand on it. Why did he have to have an X-ray and blood tests? It wasn't fair.

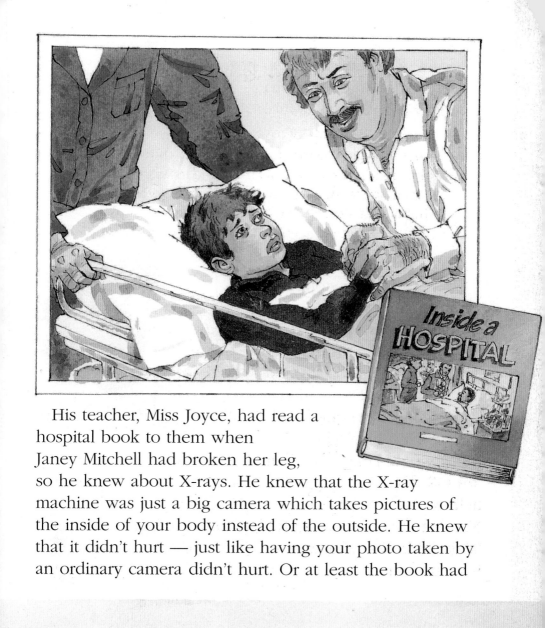

His teacher, Miss Joyce, had read a
hospital book to them when
Janey Mitchell had broken her leg,
so he knew about X-rays. He knew that the X-ray
machine was just a big camera which takes pictures of
the inside of your body instead of the outside. He knew
that it didn't hurt — just like having your photo taken by
an ordinary camera didn't hurt. Or at least the book had

said that it didn't hurt. Now he wasn't so sure.

He decided that he wasn't going to chance it. He wouldn't let anyone X-ray him. And he didn't need a blood test. He didn't know what a blood test was but he wasn't going to have one. He was going home. As soon as the man stopped pushing the trolley and went away, he would tell Da and Da would bring him back out to the car. Da wouldn't let any stupid doctor keep him here!

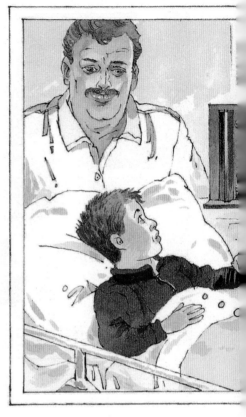

Da wouldn't listen to him, though. He let the man push the trolley into another room. And there, he let a nurse stick a thermometer into Shane's armpit. Then she wrapped a black rubber tube, like a bandage, round the top of Shane's other arm.

'Look, pet,' the nurse said, pointing to a tall box she'd

put on the table beside him: it was like a ruler standing up inside a case. 'Watch the needle; when it stops moving, it'll tell you what your blood pressure is.' She pumped air into the bandage. It squeezed his arm tighter and tighter.

Shane had once seen a nature programme where a great long snake had dropped out of a tree and looped itself in coils round a small furry animal, squeezing it to death before eating it. Now he knew what the small furry animal had felt like.

There was a hissing noise as the nurse let the air out of the bandage. The pressure went. She took the rubber bandage off his arm.

Shane didn't care what his blood pressure was.

'Let's go home, Da,' he whispered when the nurse had gone.

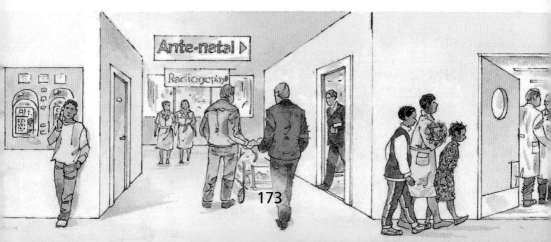

'It's all right, son. It's OK. Just be patient. The doctors know what's best. You'll get home just as soon as they make you better.'

'But I want to go home *now*!'

'Yes, Shay. I know.'

Da stroked Shane's forehead gently. Shane turned his head away.

A new nurse came over to his trolley. 'Hello …' She glanced at a piece of paper in her hand, 'er … Shane,' she said. She smiled down at him. 'We're just going to take a bit of your blood so that we can see

what's wrong with you. Only a teensie tiny drop. You won't miss it at all.'

Shane looked at the watch dangling from the pocket of her white uniform and thought of Dracula. He bet Dracula had told people they wouldn't miss a tiny drop of

their blood either.

He reached for Da's hand and held it tightly. Da squeezed his fingers back. 'It's all right, Shane. I'm here.'

The nurse rubbed the back of his hand with a pad of wet cotton wool. It was icy cold and it smelt funny. 'Look at your Daddy, Shane,' she said. 'I'm just going to give your skin a little pinch. You'll hardly feel it. OK?'

It wasn't OK.

'It'll be over in a second,' Da said. 'Be a brave boy, now, won't you?'

Shane didn't want to be brave. But, before he could pull his hand away, he felt a prick. Like a horsefly biting him. He yelped.

He turned to glare at the nurse. She was holding up a syringe with some dark browny-red liquid inside it.

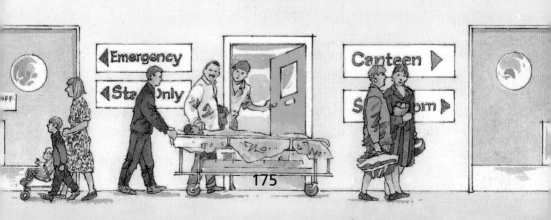

Was that his blood? She put a bit of cotton wool on to his hand where a drop of blood was just beginning to ooze out, and pressed it down hard. He tried to pull his hand away, but she held on tightly.

He felt helpless, like the boy in one of his books at home who had been caught by the master crook in a grip of steel (that was after he'd gone down to the cave under the cliffs and discovered the stolen treasure). Nurses weren't supposed to act like this, Shane thought; in his hospital book at school it said they were *nice* to you.

'There's a great boy, then,' said the first nurse.

They put a plaster on his hand and left him alone with Da.

'When are we going home, Da?' he asked, for what seemed like the thousandth time.

'Soon, Shay, soon.'

Area 1 ▶

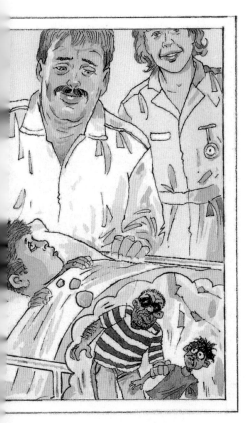

But then the man in the blue coat came back. He winked at Shane. 'Hi! How're you getting on?'

Shane didn't answer.

'I'm just taking you down to X-ray,' the man said. 'You're going to have another wee trip on the trolley, see a bit of the hospital, get your photograph taken. So you lie back and enjoy it. OK?'

Nothing was OK, but what was the point of fighting it? Nobody listened to him, not even Da.

Shane allowed himself to be wheeled down the long corridor again. Da walked beside him, holding his hand. *Why had Mammy and Daddy listened to Doctor O'Sullivan? Why had they brought him here? He'd have got better all by himself at home, if they'd only given him time.*

The man in the blue coat left him in a room full of huge machines. He winked at Shane again before he left.

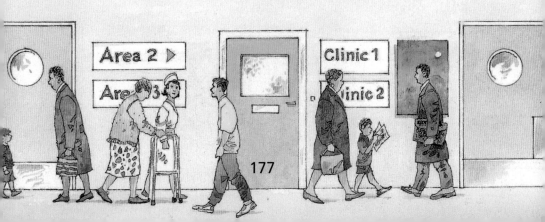

'Good luck, mate. See you later.'

'All right, Mr Walsh. You can wait outside.' Shane looked round. A bossy woman in a white coat — another nurse? — was waiting for Da to leave him here. Alone! With all these machines!

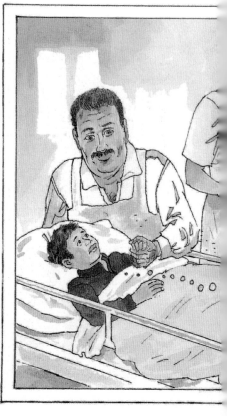

'Da ...,' he said.

'I'm staying,' Da said and squeezed his hand.

'I'm afraid that's not allowed, Mr Walsh. Shane will be quite all right. It won't take a minute.'

'I'm staying,' Da said quietly. He was twice the size of the bossy woman, Shane thought proudly.

The bossy woman sniffed. 'Then you'll have to put on a lead apron,' she said.

'That's fine by me,' Da said.

Da looked funny with a heavy white apron round him, like Nan making scones in the kitchen back home. He sat

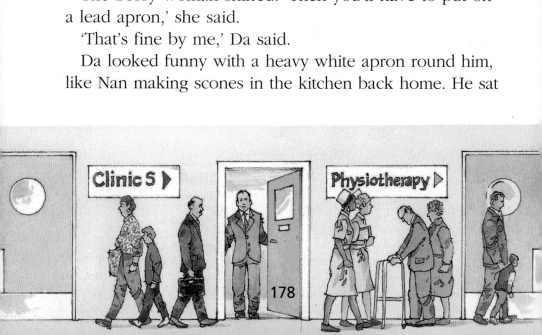

Clinic 5 ▶

Physiotherapy ▷

beside Shane and held his hand as Shane lay on a table and a machine was lowered over his sore leg until it nearly touched his skin.

'All right now, Shane. Stay absolutely still. Don't move. This is just a camera taking a picture. It doesn't hurt.'

The bossy woman and the nurse disappeared. Shane bit his lip. It was okay for people to say it was just a camera. What would happen if it fell on him? Or if the X-rays hurt as they went into his skin?

He looked up, past the machine, at the high ceiling. There was a cobweb in the corner by the window. Nan would have had something to say about that!

Then the nurse and the bossy woman came back. 'Just one more,' the bossy woman said. They made him turn so that the machine was pointing at the other side

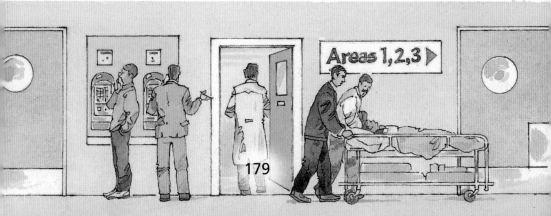

Areas 1,2,3 ▶

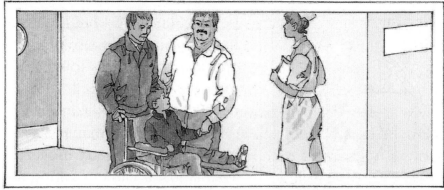

of his leg. It hurt. But at least this time Shane wasn't scared of the machine: it *was* just taking a photo, after all.

'Can I see the pictures?' he asked as the porter wheeled him out of the X-ray room.

The bossy woman actually smiled.
'You'll have to ask Doctor Azid,' she said.

They kept him in hospital for what seemed like hours. The porter in the blue coat had got him a wheelchair with a flat board sticking out in front, so that he could sit with his leg up: that way, at least, it didn't hurt.
But he was *bored*. And very, very tired. He tried to read his comics but couldn't concentrate. Instead, he listened to Diarmuid's Walkman and watched the people coming and going.

'When are we going home?' he asked Da.

'We have to wait for the result of your tests,' Da explained patiently.

Finally a nurse came and called Da into Doctor Azid's office. He was away for ages. When he came back, he looked worried.

'Are we going now?' Shane asked.

Da frowned. 'In a minute, Shay. I just have to ring Mam. You wait here while I find a phone. Be a brave boy, now. I won't be long.'

And he was gone.

Outside, night had fallen. Beyond the hospital windows, everything was black. The day seemed to have gone on forever, Shane thought; when was his daddy going to take him home?

Liza's Lamb by Margrit Cruickshank, Children's Poolbeg

Shane hates it when he has to stay in the hospital, but his mammy stays with him. When she has to go home to the farm, he becomes very upset. Gradually he makes friends with Liza, an eight year old girl who has been in the hospital for five weeks, telling her all about the animals at home on the farm and promising to give her a lamb of her own. When Shane goes home, he and Liza write to each other and Liza comes to visit the Walsh family. Find out what happens by reading *Liza's Lamb* by Margrit Cruickshank, Children's Poolbeg.

181

Blarney Blasts

1 Talk to a partner about a time when you just wanted to go home.

2 Tell a partner about a time when you were in a hospital.

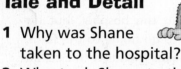

Log Jogging

Look at your Log Jogging list on page 192.

Pick one suggestion and write about it.

Tale and Detail

1 Why was Shane taken to the hospital?

2 Who took Shane to the x-ray room?

3 What was the name of the doctor at the hospital?

4 Where did the nurse place the rubber tube?

Undercover Work

1 Why did Shane not feel like being brave?

2 Why was Shane in a hurry to go home?

3 Why had the day seemed so long?

4 How did the staff at the hospital treat Shane?

5 In what ways did Shane feel that his Da was not on his side?

6 Name some things which make hissing noises.

7 What tests were done on Shane in the hospital?

Word Wizardry

The **doing** words in sentences are very important. Put the **doing** words below back into the sentences.

rubbed   push   biting   squeezed   winked

1 He let the man _____ the trolley into another room.

2 It _____ his arm tighter and tighter.

3 The nurse _____ the back of his hand with a pad of wet cotton.

4 It was like a horsefly _____ him.

5 He _____ at Shane.

Surf the Imagination

1 Imagine you are a scientist who invents something which will help people. Draw a diagram of your invention and write about it.

2 Write about hospital. Say how you feel.

Mouse Search

1 What do you need to eat to stay healthy?

2 What makes your blood move around your body?

3 Some illnesses are ones that you will not get because you have been vaccinated against them. Find out what vaccinations you have had.

A sudden puff of glittering smoke

Jeanie sat at her desk, twisting the ring on her finger round and round. The ring was bothering her terribly. It was so tight she couldn't get it off. She'd only found it a couple of hours before, glinting so brightly in the gutter she was astonished no one else had noticed it. She'd picked it up and looked around, wondering what to do. Then, when the school bell rang, she'd pushed it hastily onto a finger and run the last few yards into the playground.

But in her hurry she had shoved it on the wrong finger. Now she'd been struggling with it all through register.

'Call out your name if you are having a school dinner today,' ordered Mr Piper.

'David!'

'Asha!'

'William!'

'Jeanie!'

As she called out her name, she couldn't help giving the ring another little twist.

There was a sudden puff of glittering smoke, and the ring was spinning on the desk in front of her. Jeanie drew her hand away smartly, and stared in wonder.

Before her eyes, the smoke turned to a column of glistening fog, then formed a spinning ball, then took — slowly, slowly — a strange and ancient shape.

It was a genie.

No doubt about it. He was no taller than her pencil and mist still curled around him, but he looked like every genie she had ever seen in books: a little fat in the belly, with a silk bodice and billowing pantaloons

185

that looked for all the
world as if they had been
woven from silver shifting mists.
Tiny stars winked all over them, and they
were held up by a belt of pure gold.
On his feet were the tiniest curly slippers,
with pointed ends.

Folding his arms, the genie bowed low.

'Greetings,' he said.

Jeanie just stared, scarcely believing
what she saw. She gave herself a little
shake, and looked around the classroom.
But nobody else seemed to have noticed
this odd little creature standing in a pool
of mist on her desk.

Extraordinary!

Was she dreaming? Was it possible?
Had some old, old magic come her way?

'Who are you?' she whispered.

'I am the genie of the ring,' the small
apparition with the folded arms declared.
'You called me.'

'*I* called you?'

'*Genie*, you called.'

'Not G-e-n-i-e! *J-e-a-n-i-e!*'

The creature shrugged.

'One little mistake,' he said. 'Even a genie gets rusty after five hundred years stuck in a ring.'

'Five hundred years!'

Jeanie was horrified. She felt sorry enough for herself, stuck in the classroom all day. But five hundred years stuck in a ring!

The genie, however, simply waved a hand, lightly dismissing whole lifetimes left unlived.

'Where Hope is lost, Patience must reign. In the end there will always be someone.'

'And it was me! So now you're *mine*.'

The genie looked her up and down coolly, and raised his eyebrows. Jeanie blushed. She wished she had taken the trouble that morning to put on something fancier than her plain shirt and faded jeans. To judge from the shimmering finery the genie wore, he had been used to far better days and far richer places.

But it wasn't her clothes he was noticing, but her bad manners.

'You do not *own* me,' he corrected her sternly. 'I serve the ring. It just so happens you were wearing it.'

Now Jeanie blushed even more deeply.

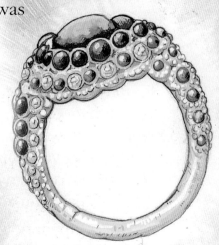

Blarney Blasts

1 Imagine that you found a magic ring. Talk to a partner about what you would wish for.

2 Jeanie blushed and blushed again. Why do you think she felt embarrassed? Talk to a partner about it and about a time you felt embarrassed.

Log Jogging

Look at your Log Jogging list on page 192.

Pick one suggestion and write about it.

Tale and Detail

1 Where did Jeanie find the ring?
2 How tall was the genie?
3 For how many years had the genie been stuck inside the ring?
4 What was Jeanie wearing?
5 How did the ring feel to touch?

Undercover Work

1 Explain the accident that cause the genie to appear.
2 At what time of the day does this story take place? How do you know?
3 Describe the genie. Say what he looked like and what kind of person he was.
4 Why did Jeanie wish that she had worn different clothes to school that day?

Word Wizardry

Put these words into the sentences.
Try to do them without looking in the story.

he   She   He   it   his   herself   him   her   she

1 Jeanie sat at _____ desk, twisting the ring
on _____ finger.

2 _____ was no taller than _____ pencil.

3 Folding _____ arms, the genie bowed low.

4 Was _____ dreaming? Was _____ possible?

5 _____ felt sorry enough for _____, stuck in the
classroom all day.

Surf the Imagination

1 Draw your own genie.
2 What do you think Jeanie wished for?
3 If a genie offered you just one wish,
   what would you choose? Write about it.
4 Jeanie did not wear a uniform to school.
   Design and draw a school uniform for
   the girls and boys in her school.

Mouse Search

1 Look around your classroom.
   List as many things as you can
   which are made from wood.
2 Find the other story about
   wishes in this book.
3 Another story that has a genie
   in it is *Ali Baba and the Forty
   Thieves*. Read that story.

191

Here are some suggestions to help you think about the story you have just read.

Pick one of them. Write about it.

If this is taking a lot of time to write, discuss with your teacher what you are to do about the other activity sections for the story.

Log Jogging

. . . .

This story reminds me of...

As I read the story I felt...

My favourite character is...

I liked/disliked this story because...

My favourite moment in the story was...

I wonder why...

I felt sorry for...

Poetry

Acknowledgements

The publishers gratefully acknowledge the following for permission
to reproduce copyright material:

Oxford University Press for 'If All the Seas', Anon;
Julie Holder for 'The Alien' by Julie Holder from *A Third Poetry Book*,
    compiled by John Foster and published by Oxford University Press;
Egmont Children's Books Ltd for 'Gorilla' by Martin Honeysett
    from *Another First Poetry Book*, published by Oxford University Press;
A P Watt Ltd Literary Agents, on behalf of Michael B Yeats,
    for 'To a Squirrel at Kyle-na-no' by W B Yeats;
John Kitching for 'Request' by John Kitching from *Another Fourth Poetry Book*,
    published by Oxford University Press;
Edite Kroll Literary Agency for 'Zebra Question'
    from *A Light in the Attic* by Shel Silverstein Copyright © 1981 by Evil Eye Music, Inc.

Every effort has been made to secure permission to reproduce copyright material in
this book. If the publishers have inadvertently overlooked any copyright holders,
however, they will be pleased to come to a suitable arrangement with them at the
earliest opportunity.

Contents

If All the Seas

If all the seas were one sea,
What a great sea that would be!
If all the trees were one tree,
What a great tree that would be!
And if all the axes were one axe,
What a great axe that would be!
And if all the men were one man,
What a great man that would be!
And if the great man took the great axe
And cut down the great tree,
And let it fall into the great sea,
What a splish-splash that would be!

Anon

Wasps

Wasps like coffee.
Syrup.
Tea.
Coco-cola.
Butter.
Me.

Dorothy Aldis

A Blink

A blink, I think, is the same as a wink,
A blink is a wink that grew,
For a *wink* you blink with only one eye,
And a *blink* you wink with two!

Jacqueline Segal

2

The Rabbit and the Fox

A RABBIT came hopping, hopping,
Hopping along in the park.
'I've just been shopping, shopping,
I must be home before dark.'

A fox came stalking, stalking,
Stalking from under a tree.
'Where are you walking, walking?
Why don't you walk with me?'

The rabbit went hopping, hopping,
Hopping away from the tree.
'I've just been shopping, shopping,
I must be home for my tea.'

'Come with me, bunny, bunny —
Bunny, you come with me;
I'll give you some honey, honey,
I'll give you some honey for tea.'

'I can't be stopping, stopping,
I'm far too busy today' —
And the rabbit went hopping, hopping,
Hopping away and away.

Clive Sansom

The Alien

The alien
Was as round as the moon.
Five legs he had
And his ears played a tune.
His hair was pink
And his knees were green,
He was the funniest thing I'd seen
As he danced in the door
Of his strange spacecraft,
He looked at me —
And laughed and laughed!

Julie Holder

4

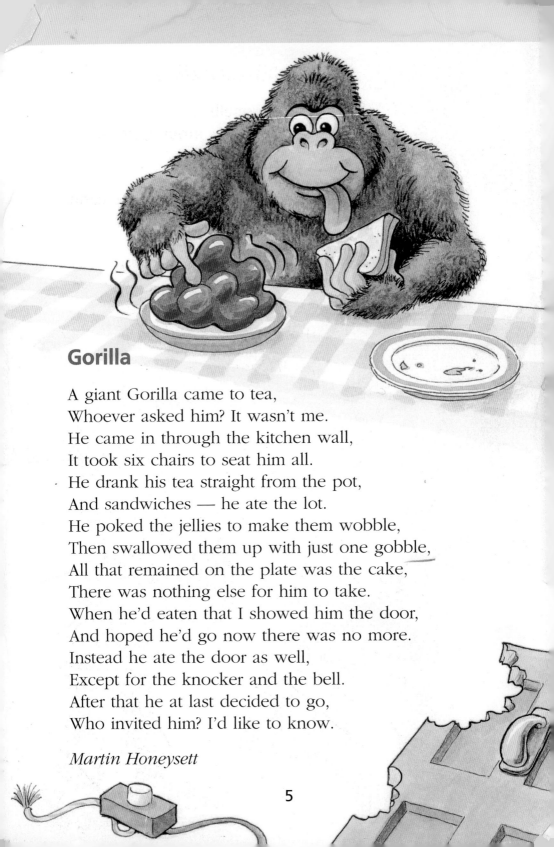

Gorilla

A giant Gorilla came to tea,
Whoever asked him? It wasn't me.
He came in through the kitchen wall,
It took six chairs to seat him all.
He drank his tea straight from the pot,
And sandwiches — he ate the lot.
He poked the jellies to make them wobble,
Then swallowed them up with just one gobble,
All that remained on the plate was the cake,
There was nothing else for him to take.
When he'd eaten that I showed him the door,
And hoped he'd go now there was no more.
Instead he ate the door as well,
Except for the knocker and the bell.
After that he at last decided to go,
Who invited him? I'd like to know.

Martin Honeysett

5

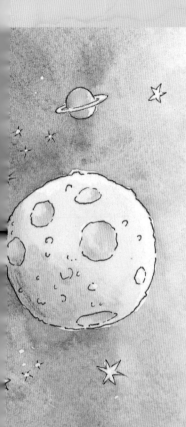

Satellite, satellite

Satellite, satellite,
The earth goes around the sun.

Satellite, satellite,
The moon goes around the earth.

Satellite, satellite,
I have a little satellite:

My little brother orbits me
And pesters day and night.

Eve Merrian

To a Squirrel at Kyle-na-no

COME play with me;
Why should you run
Through the shaking tree
As though I'd a gun
To strike you dead?
When all I would do
Is to scratch your head
And let you go.

W B Yeats

Request

I pray you, teacher,
Teach me so
That I will always
Want to know.

John Kitching

Zebra Question

I asked the zebra,
Are you black with white stripes?
Or white with black stripes?
And the zebra asked me,
Are you good with bad habits?
Or are you bad with good habits?
Are you noisy with quiet times?
Or are you quiet with noisy times?
Are you happy with some sad days?
Or are you sad with some happy days?
Are you neat with some sloppy ways?
Or are you sloppy with some neat ways?
And on and on and on and on
And on and on he went.
I'll never ask a zebra
About stripes
Again.

Shel Silverstein

8

American nursery rhymes

WHEN I am President
   Of these United States,
I'll eat up all the candy
   And swing on all the gates.

FUZZY Wuzzy was a bear,
   A bear was Fuzzy Wuzzy.
When Fuzzy Wuzzy lost his hair
   He wasn't fuzzy, was he?

THERE was an old owl who lived in an oak;
The more he heard, the less he spoke.
The less he spoke, the more he heard.
Why aren't we like that wise old bird!

OLD Joe Brown, he had a wife,
  She was all of eight feet tall.
She slept with her head in the kitchen,
  And her feet stuck out in the hall.

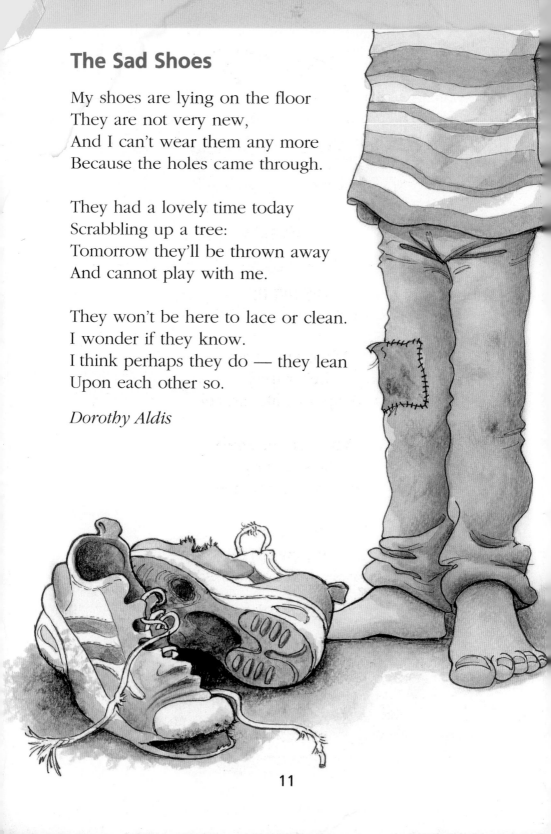

The Sad Shoes

My shoes are lying on the floor
They are not very new,
And I can't wear them any more
Because the holes came through.

They had a lovely time today
Scrabbling up a tree:
Tomorrow they'll be thrown away
And cannot play with me.

They won't be here to lace or clean.
I wonder if they know.
I think perhaps they do — they lean
Upon each other so.

Dorothy Aldis

My Puppy

IT's funny
my puppy
knows just how I feel.

When I'm happy
he's yappy
and squirms like an eel.

When I'm grumpy
he's slumpy
and stays at my heel.

It's funny
my puppy
knows such a great deal.

Aileen Fisher

My Playmate

I often wonder how it is
   That on a rainy day,
A little boy, just like myself,
   Comes out with me to play.

And we step in all the puddles
   When walking into town,
But though I stand the right way up,
   He's always upside-down.

I have to tread upon his feet,
   Which is a sorry sight,
With my right foot on his left foot,
   My left foot on his right.

I really wish he'd talk to me,
   He seems so very kind,
For when I look and smile at him
   He does the same, I find.

But I never hear him speaking,
   So surely he must be
In some strange land the other side,
   Just opposite to me.

Mary I Osborn

13